MATHS*DIRE*

Book D

Jean Cheshire
Christine Collins
Mark Pepper
Anne White

Series Editor: **Mundher Adhami**

Collins Educational

An imprint of HarperCollins*Publishers*

Contents

Published by Collins Educational
An imprint of HarperCollinsPublishers Ltd
77-85 Fulham Palace Road
London W6 8JB

The HarperCollins website address is www.**fire**and**water**.com
© HarperCollinsPublishers Ltd 1999
First published 1999
ISBN 0 00 322493 7

Mundher Adhami, Jean Cheshire, Christine Collins, Mark Pepper and
Anne White assert the moral right to be identified as the authors of this work.

British Library Cataloguing in Publication Data
A catalogue record for this book is available from the British Library.

Edited by Dodi Beardshaw
Picture research by Caroline Thompson
Design by Chi Leung
Commissioning Editor: Alison Walters
Cover photographs: Tony Stone Images and Accurist
Illustrations by Barking Dog Art, Russell Birkett, Phillip Burrows, Hardlines,
Peter Harper, Bethan Matthews, Sylvie Poggio Agency (Lisa Smith)
and Harry Venning
Production by James Graves
Printed and bound by Scotprint, Musselburgh.

Acknowledgements

Every effort has been made to contact the holders of copyright material, but
if any have been inadvertently overlooked the publishers will be pleased to
make the necessary arrangements at the first opportunity.

The publishers would like to thank the following for permission to reproduce
photographs (T = Top, B = Bottom, C = Centre, L= Left, R = Right):

Advertising Archives, 104;
Allsport/S Botterill, 29, E Shaw, 89;
A Messinis Stringer/Associated Press, 13;
BBC Photograph Library, 10, 59, 68;
The construction of a church dedicated to St Michael by Master of
Avila/Avila Cathedral, Castilla-Leon, Spain/Index/Bridgeman Art Library, 96;
V Miles/Environmental Images, 31;
Express Newspapers Ltd, 23;
Freight Photo Library, 102;
Michael Holford, 52;
Images Colour Library, 6L;
Andrew Lambert, 8, 42, 44, 118, 124;
NASA, 6R, 50;
B Goodale/Oxford Scientific Films Ltd, 38;
Popperfoto, 27;
(c) The Post Office, 83;
Rex Features Ltd, 18R, 70, 73, 81, 91, 98;
Science & Society Picture Library, 115;
Skyscan Photo Library, 54;
Tony Stone Images, 18L, 21, 34, 47, 57;
Telegraph Colour Library, 25, 40, 78, 106, 121;

Module D1

Number and time

1 What's the date, mate?
Writing the date in figures and words, according to use

2 A calendar or a diary?
Using a calendar and a diary to make appointments and calculate time intervals

3 Grandfather clocks
Reading an analogue clock to the nearest minute, using and interpreting a variety of words to say these times

4 Short-term estimates
Estimating the time taken for a familiar activity, using seconds or minutes

5 Which clock time?
Converting 24 hour clock time to 12 hour clock time and vice versa

6 Dates and times skills
Using and applying skills in reading and interpreting dates and times

Key words and phrases

accuracy
convert
estimate
ordinal numbers: first, second, third
quarter, half
to the nearest

six-digit dates
months of the year
days of the week
12 hour clock
24 hour clock
a.m./p.m.
hour, o'clock
seconds, minutes

1 What's the date, mate?

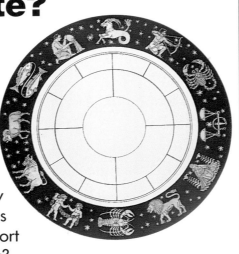

What's the date, mate? Our calendar is divided into twelve months. The sun and moon move in regular patterns around the Earth. Why do the months have different lengths? Which two months that follow each other are both long ones of 31 days? Are there two short months that follow each other?

1. Sometimes we need to write months as numbers. For example, April is written as 04 because it is the fourth month. What is the number for each of these months? Remember to write it as a two-digit number.

   a November   c June   e February
   b March   d August   f October

2. Convert today's date to a six-digit date.
3. Write your date of birth as a word date and a six-digit date. Do the same for the date of birth of three friends.
4. Write Christmas Day as a word date and a six-digit date.

Is the party on 3rd October 2,000, or 03.10.00?

Sharon carries out a survey of primary school pupils. She asks them their birthday and enters it as a pair of two-digit numbers

| 0 | 5 | . | 1 | 1 |

What should she write for these birthdays?
1. 24 September
2. 30 December
3. 19 February
4. 4 November
5. 7 July
6. 25 May
7. 9 April

My birthday is on 5 November.

C

Mrs Rasson is a Year 8 form tutor. At the start of each month she has a celebration for all the pupils who have a birthday in that month. Here are the dates of birth for her form. Sort them into month headings – January, February, and so on.

12.09.87	11.05.88	24.08.87	15.03.88	30.08.87	27.10.87
01.06.88	31.11.87	22.09.87	16.06.88	23.07.88	11.04.88
26.07.88	23.05.88	08.04.88	20.02.88	19.01.88	29.09.87
13.01.88	04.08.87	22.06.88	30.12.87	07.11.87	01.01.88

D

Alice has to add the dates of her school terms and holidays to an application form. She must enter the dates as a six-digit number, with two digits for the day, two for the month, and two for the year. How should she write the 12 dates on the form?

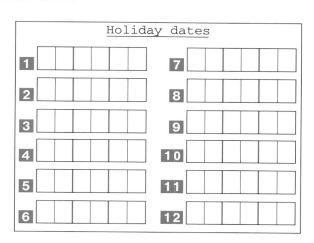

STROUD HIGH

Dates for your diary

- ·Autumn term opens Tues 7th Sept 2000
- ·Half term 25th Oct—29th Oct
- ·Autumn term closes Wed 22 Dec 2000
- ·Spring term starts Weds 5th Jan 2001
- ·Half term 21—25th Feb
- ·Spring term closes Fri 14th April
- ·Summer term opens Weds 3rd May
- ·Half term 29th May-2nd June
- ·Summer term closes Fri 21st July

Holiday dates

1 | 2 | 3 | 4 | 5 | 6 |
7 | 8 | 9 | 10 | 11 | 12 |

E

If today's date is May 4th 2000 say whether these 'money off' vouchers are still valid or not?

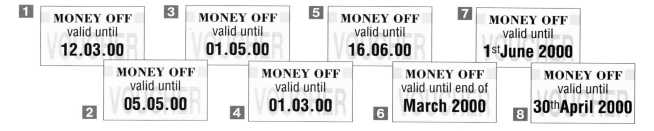

1 MONEY OFF valid until **12.03.00**

3 MONEY OFF valid until **01.05.00**

5 MONEY OFF valid until **16.06.00**

7 MONEY OFF valid until **1ˢᵗ June 2000**

2 MONEY OFF valid until **05.05.00**

4 MONEY OFF valid until **01.03.00**

6 MONEY OFF valid until end of **March 2000**

8 MONEY OFF valid until **30ᵗʰ April 2000**

Now look back on your work in this lesson.
- Can you read and write the date in two different ways?
- Give four examples of where you might see these two different ways of writing the date.

② A calendar or a diary?

What kinds of calendars do you use at home?
Do you use a different kind at school?
Do you prefer small or large calendars? Why?

Today's date is the 14th of September.

1. Simon's library book is exactly one week late. What date was it due back?
2. He takes the book back and takes out a new book which is due back in exactly two weeks. What date is the new book due back?
3. It is Simon's turn to wash the football kit on the third Saturday of each month. Does he have to wash it today?
4. What was the date when he last had to wash it?
5. How many weeks is it until he has to wash it next?
6. On the last Monday of each month Simon weeds his granny's garden. Will he do the garden next week?
7. What is the date of the next two Mondays when he will do the garden?

Rashid is paid on the first Thursday of each month and Sally is paid on the last Wednesday of each month. Use this year's calendar to write down the dates on which Rashid and Sally will be paid for the next 6 months.

Anil has diabetes. He visits the hospital to have his blood checked. Here are his appointments. How many weeks are there between each pair of appointments?

APPOINTMENT CARD	
Name: Anil	
Date:	
3rd March	
10th March	
24th March	
28th April	
23rd June	

After her baby is born, Tracey must go to the clinic after two weeks, then after another three weeks, and then again after another 12 weeks.

If her first appointment is on June 2nd, when will her next two appointments be?

Late library books are charged at 20p per whole week after their due date. How many whole weeks are these books late?

Date due Day.Month.Year	Today's date Day.Month.Year	Whole weeks late
1 03.08.00	18.08.00	↻
2 26.01.00	19.02.00	↻
3 10.03.00	19.03.00	↻
4 16.05.00	01.06.00	↻
5 22.09.00	21.10.00	↻
6 02.11.00	10.12.00	↻
7 13.02.00	18.02.00	↻
8 29.07.00	03.09.00	↻

A car collected on the evening of 3 August and returned on the evening of 10 August is charged for seven days. The days charged are: 4 August, 5 August, 6 August, 7 August, 8 August, 9 August, 10 August. Use your calendar to work out the missing entries in this table.

Collected on the evening of	Returned on the evening of	Weeks and days	Days charged
1 2 July	19 July	2 weeks 3 days	17
2 10 Aug	2 Sept	☆	☆
3 3 May	☆	3 weeks	☆
4 ☆	10 July	☆	12
5 21 Mar	27 April	☆	☆
6 24 Jan	☆	☆	19

Now look back on your work in this lesson.
- Can you use a calendar to count on in days and weeks?
- Can you count past the end of the month?

③ Grandfather clocks

Zoë is just about to give another time check on the radio. She often uses phrases like quarter to and 10 minutes past, without numbers.

Why do you think the round face and hands of the old clocks are still popular?

A

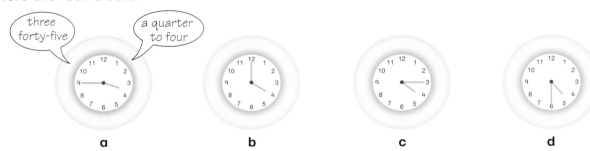

Here are four clocks.

three forty-five   *a quarter to four*

a   b   c   d

1 Say each of these times in two ways. The first one is done for you.

2 What would you say for one minute after each of these times?

3 Say the time for every ten minutes between four and five o'clock, in two different ways. Start with *Four ten* and *Ten past four.*

4 What would you say for each of these times two minutes later?

B

Ena is the DJ for the hospital radio each Saturday. Her script tells her to repeat her time checks in two ways.

It's a quarter to 8, 7:45 and now for the new number one.

a   b   c   d   e   f

1 Write a speech bubble for Ena's time checks for each of the following. You can choose a record for her to play as well!

C

Here are Ena's speech bubbles. Draw the position of the hands on the clock face when she makes these time checks.

1 Good morning! It's 8:20, that's twenty past 8, and we're playing a birthday request.

2 It's 8:45, a quarter to 9, and it's freezing cold out. We're in the best place here!

3 It's 9:35, that's twenty-five minutes to 10. Thanks for all your notes this week. Let's read some of them now.

4 It's quarter past ten, 10:15, morning coffee will be coming soon...

5 Sadly, it's my last record at 10:55, five to 11. I'll be here again next week.

D

For each clock time given in numbers, choose the clock face with the same time and write the time in words.

1 11:23
2 9:47
3 8:17
4 10:22
5 12:18
6 3:52

E

Malik's watch has stopped. He phones the talking clock and sets his watch to the right time. Draw a clock face with hands in the correct position if the talking clock says:

1 'At the third stroke the time will be eleven forty-three and ten seconds.'

2 'At the third stroke the time will be eight twelve and twenty seconds.'

3 'At the third stroke the time will be ten fifty-four and ten seconds.'

4 'At the third stroke the time will be four thirty-two and twenty seconds.'

5 'At the third stroke the time will be five twenty-eight and twenty seconds.'

6 'At the third stroke the time will be one thirty-seven and 10 seconds.'

F

Elsie has to catch the morning train to meet her friends. The pictures show the station clock and the time of the next train. How long does Elsie have to wait for each train?

1

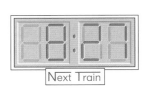
Next Train

4

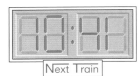
Next Train

2

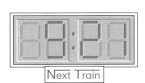
Next Train

5

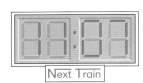
Next Train

3

Next Train

6

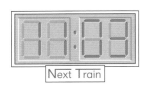
Next Train

Now look back on your work in this lesson.
- Can you read the time on a clock face to the nearest minute?
- Can you say the time in two different ways?

4 Short-term estimates

The world record for the 100 m sprint is held by Maurice Greene at just below 10 seconds. Hold your breath and slowly count from 1 to 10 while imagining the sprinters doing the race. Why is it difficult to imagine this time record getting lower?

1 How long do you think you can hold your breath – a few seconds? a few minutes? Working with a partner, write down a guess and then time each other.

2 How long do you think you can keep your eyes open without blinking – a few seconds? a few minutes? Working with a partner, write down a guess and then time each other.

3 How long do you think you can stand on one leg without support – a few seconds? a few minutes? Working with a partner, write down a guess and then time each other.

4 How long do you think you can stand on your tip-toes without support – a few seconds? a few minutes? Working with a partner, write down a guess and then time each other.

Can you estimate when ten seconds has passed? Work with a partner like this:

Estimate six times each and make a table for yourself. The first one is done for you.

Guess	Number of seconds	Number of seconds over or under
1	8	2
2	✳	✳
3	✳	✳
5	✳	✳
6	✳	✳
7	✳	✳

8 Did your guessing improve?

9 Which of you was better at estimating 10 seconds?

1. Make another table like the one in exercise B but say minutes instead of seconds. Has your guessing improved?
2. Which of you was better at estimating one minute?

Do some more estimating.

1. How long do you think it would take to empty your schoolbag, throw away any rubbish and put your things back in neatly? Write down your guess and then time yourself doing the job. How far off was your guess?
2. How long do you think it would take to remove your shoes and put them back on? Write down your guess and then time yourself doing the job. How far off was your guess?
3. How long do you think it would take to write down the names of all the people in your row of desks or at your table? Write down your guess and then time yourself doing the job. How far off was your guess?

Put these activities in the correct column.

A few seconds	A few minutes	More than ten minutes

1. Brushing your teeth
2. Getting dressed for school
3. Preparing an evening meal
4. Making a slice of toast
5. Passing the sauce at the meal table
6. Answering a ringing phone
7. Getting into a car and putting on your seatbelt
8. Unloading the supermarket shopping from bags into the cupboards
9. Washing up after breakfast
10. Doing the ironing for your family

Now look back on your work in this lesson.
- Try to estimate how long ten seconds is. How close were you?
- Have your estimates become more accurate during the lesson?

⑤ Which clock time?

One of these clocks must be wrong.
What should the digital 24 hour clock show if the round clock is correct?
What should the round clock show if the digital clock is correct?

Answer these time problems.

> Looneytoons 4:45, Storytime 16:10, Cartoon Capers 5:05,
> Byker Grove 17:35, Newsround 4:30, Rugrats 16:25

1 Here are some afternoon children's TV programmes. The times are written either in the 24 hour or the 12 hour clock. Write the times in order, starting with the earliest.

Ben 11:40 p.m. Malik 00:10 ANIL midnight Haq 2 a.m. Elsie 23:50 Carol 23:35

2 Six friends are arguing about who has been to bed the latest. They all agree to write their latest bedtime this month on a piece of paper. Sort them into order, starting with the latest.

I started at 10:00. (Saida)
I can't start until 13:00. (Sara)
I'm planning to start at 14:00. (Meena)
My mother says I should start at 17:00. (Ayesha)
I began at 18:30. (Sally)
I didn't start until 20:10. (Joanne)

3 At the weekend six pupils each have two hours of homework. Here are their start times, using the 24 hour clock. What time will each one finish?

4 Write the time for the next six 10 minute intervals, starting from the times given.

a 10:20, 10:30, _____, _____, _____, _____, _____, _____

b 16:40, 16:50, _____, _____, _____, _____, _____, _____

c 23:30, 23:40, _____, _____, _____, _____, _____, _____

d 12:20, 12:30, _____, _____, _____, _____, _____, _____

Here is a section from a TV listings magazine. Binoy has marked the programmes he wants to record.

Sky Moviemax

6.00 a.m. Medicine River
8.00 Godzilla vs Gigan
10.00 Deep Family Secrets
12.00 Medicine River
2.00 Godzilla vs Gigan
4.00 Here comes the Son
6.00 Friendship's Field
8.00 Smoke
10.00 The Funeral
11.45 Movietalk
12.15 Nixon
3.25 The Plaque

Sky Premier

6.30 a.m. Horses and Champions
8.30 Forbidden Territory: Stanley's search for Livingstone

10.30 Agatha Christie's The Man in the Brown Suit
12.30 Hollywood Buzz
1.00 Horses and Champions
3.00 Forbidden Territory: Stanley's search for Livingstone
5.00 Clubhouse Detectives
7.00 The Santa Clause
9.00 Barry Norman's Film Night
9.30 Free Money
11.05 Blood and Wine
12.50 Diabolique
2.40 On Seventh Avenue
4.10 The Santa Clause

Sky Cinema

11.00 a.m. Francis in the Haunted House
12.15 A Farewell to Arms

2.45 The Great Dictator
4.45 The White Tower
6.30 The Racket
8.00 The Lighthorsemen
10.00 Catch-22
12.05 The Hustler
2.20 The Batchelor Party
3.55–5.15 Three Hours to Kill

FilmFour

7.00 p.m. FilmFour Launch
7.15 What's eating Gilbert Grape
9.30 Nothing is what it seems
10.00 The Usual Suspects
12.00 Desserts
12.10 The Pillow Book
2.30 Caro Diario
4.25–5.50 Crystal Voyager

1 Binoy's video recorder uses 24 hour time. What start times should he set for each programme?

Ramon lives in Cambridge. He plans to meet a friend at the station in London at half past four.

Cambridge	Dep	11.45	12.15	12.27	12.45	13.15	13.27	13.45	14.15
London Kings X	Arr	12.36	13.06	13.28	13.36	14.06	14.28	14.36	15.06

Cambridge	Dep	14.27	14.45	15.15	15.27	15.45	16.15	16.27	16.45
London Kings X	Arr	15.28	15.36	16.06	16.28	16.36	17.06	17.28	17.36

London Kings X	Dep	18.51	19.15	19.45	19.51	20.06	20.51	21.06	21.51
Cambridge	Arr	19.54	20.04	20.34	20.54	21.25	21.53	22.25	22.53

London Kings X	Dep	22.06	23.15	23.58					
Cambridge	Arr	23.25	00.07	00.56					

1 Ramon can't leave until after 2:30 p.m. Which three trains could he aim to catch?

2 He leaves London after 10 p.m. Which three trains could he get home?

Fiona is a traffic warden. She is checking the Pay and Display car park. The stickers show the time the driver has paid up to.

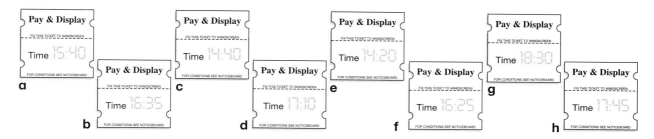

a — Pay & Display — FIX THIS TICKET TO WINDSCREEN — Time 15:40 — FOR CONDITIONS SEE NOTICEBOARD

b — Pay & Display — FIX THIS TICKET TO WINDSCREEN — Time 16:35 — FOR CONDITIONS SEE NOTICEBOARD

c — Pay & Display — FIX THIS TICKET TO WINDSCREEN — Time 14:40 — FOR CONDITIONS SEE NOTICEBOARD

d — Pay & Display — FIX THIS TICKET TO WINDSCREEN — Time 17:10 — FOR CONDITIONS SEE NOTICEBOARD

e — Pay & Display — FIX THIS TICKET TO WINDSCREEN — Time 14:20 — FOR CONDITIONS SEE NOTICEBOARD

f — Pay & Display — FIX THIS TICKET TO WINDSCREEN — Time 16:25 — FOR CONDITIONS SEE NOTICEBOARD

g — Pay & Display — FIX THIS TICKET TO WINDSCREEN — Time 18:30 — FOR CONDITIONS SEE NOTICEBOARD

h — Pay & Display — FIX THIS TICKET TO WINDSCREEN — Time 17:45 — FOR CONDITIONS SEE NOTICEBOARD

1 If it is now four-thirty p.m., which cars will she put a parking ticket on?

Olga has to check in for her flight two hours before it leaves. The travel agent gives her a selection of flight times and she makes a table. Copy the table and fill in the gaps. The first one is done for you.

Flight time (24 hour)	Flight time (12 hour)	Check in time
1 16:40	4:40 p.m.	2:40 p.m.
2 17:10	✳	✳
3 18:30	✳	✳
4 20:05	✳	✳
5 22:20	✳	✳
6 23:45	✳	✳

Carl has made a train journey on each day of his holiday. He has written the start time from the station clock as the train pulled out and the finish time from the station clock as his train pulled in. Complete the table by filling in the length of each journey.

Start time	Finish time	How long?
1 3 p.m.	17:40	✳
2 14:30	4:50 p.m.	✳
3 17:10	9:30 p.m.	✳
4 11:20 a.m.	14:30	✳

Now look back on your work in this lesson.
- Show how you can convert 24 hour times to 12 hour times, and vice versa.
- Give examples of places where you need to use 24 hour times.

⑥ Dates and times skills

This photo of Niagara Falls was taken at 5 o'clock in the afternoon. Moscow is eight hours ahead of Niagara Falls. What time do you think the photo of St Basil's Cathedral in Moscow was taken?

A

1. Write today's date in words and as a six-digit date.
2. What will be the date three weeks from today?
3. What date was it five weeks ago?
4. What will be the date on Saturday?
5. What is the time now? Write it as both a 12 hour time and as a four-digit 24 hour time.
6. What time will it be in three hours from now? Write it as both a 12 hour time and as a four-digit 24 hour time.

B

Sarah carries out a survey of holidays. She asks people which date they want to start their holiday on. She enters it as a pair of two-digit numbers on the data sheet. What should she write for these start dates?

1. 26 July   ☐☐.☐☐
2. 23 May   ☐☐.☐☐
3. 14 Aug   ☐☐.☐☐
4. 29 Sept   ☐☐.☐☐
5. 12 June   ☐☐.☐☐
6. 23 Mar   ☐☐.☐☐
7. 17 July   ☐☐.☐☐
8. 16 Jan   ☐☐.☐☐

C

Ebony must pay her credit card on the third Wednesday of each month. She gets paid on the second Monday of each month. Use this year's calendar to write down when Ebony must pay her credit card and when she will be paid, for each of the next six months.

At the school parent's evening each parent has an appointment to see the form teacher. The teacher calls out the time and the parent who has that time goes in. Who should go in for each of these calls?

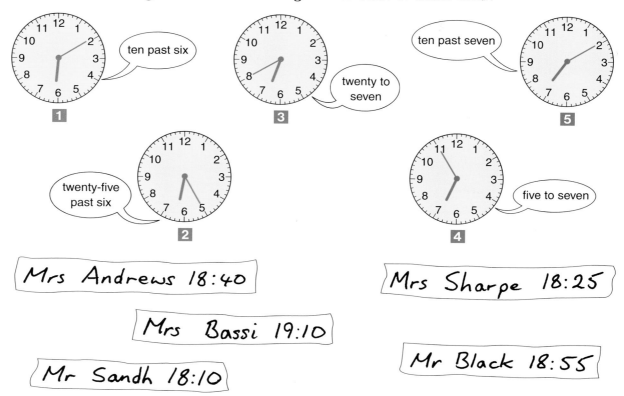

Mrs Andrews 18:40

Mrs Sharpe 18:25

Mrs Bassi 19:10

Mr Black 18:55

Mr Sandh 18:10

How close are you to being correct?

1. Estimate how long it would take you to write down the name, address and telephone number of three of your friends. Now time yourself doing this.

2. Estimate how long it would take you to put these numbers in order smallest to largest.

| 27 | 3027 | 286 | 5610 | 10 000 | 40008 | 0.26 | 3245 | 800 | 6007 |

Now time yourself doing this.

3. Estimate how long it would take you to write out the answers to the 5×, 6×, 7×, and 8× tables. Now time yourself doing this.

4. Estimate how long it would take you to write down all the months of the year and the number of days in them. Now time yourself doing this.

Now look back on your work in this lesson.
- Show that you can read and write the date and time in different ways.
- How would you enter a series of appointments on a calendar or electronic organiser?

Module D2

Handling data

❶ **Plotting line graphs**
Plotting and joining points to form a continuous graph

❷ **Reading graphs**
Reading the values of a graph in whole numbers at a specified point on the graph

❸ **Overall shape of graphs**
Interpreting a single general trend on a graph

❹ **Devise a bar chart**
Drawing and interpreting a bar chart using data that is in discrete categories

❺ **Even chances**
Understanding and using the idea of *evens* and saying whether events are more or less likely

❻ **Skills in graphs**
Practising drawing and interpreting a variety of graphs

Key words and phrases

bars across, down or up
greatest value
horizontal and vertical axes
least value
line graph
plot
points

continuous
overall shape of a graph
rising or falling line

50–50
better than evens
equal chances
even chance
evens
worse than evens

❶ Plotting line graphs

This is a photograph of Lefkas, one of the Greek islands.
Have you ever been to Greece or elsewhere in the Mediterranean?
Why would some people prefer to live in such places?
Does having a warm climate mean the temperature never changes?

 John and his family went to Greece for a holiday. He noticed that it was not always as hot as he imagined. He recorded the temperature at noon every day. Here are his findings.

Day	Temperature/°C
Mon	22
Tues	26
Wed	24
Thurs	30
Fri	28
Sat	26

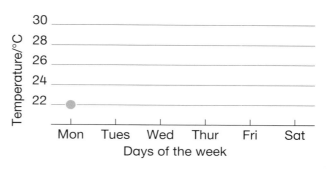

1 Copy the graph on to squared paper. Place a small cross or a point above the mark for noon for each day. The first one is done for you. Then join them together.

 Sandra's mum had a baby daughter. One of Sandra's jobs was to weigh the baby and record her weight. Here are her findings.

Age/months	Weight/kg
2	5
4	6
6	6
8	8
10	9
12	11

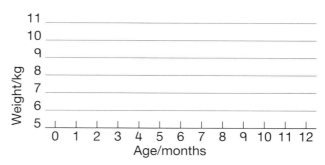

1 Copy the graph on to squared paper. Plot the points and then join them together.

Fahema did a science experiment in which she measured the temperature outside her classroom every two hours and wrote down her findings. Here are her results.

Time	Temperature/°C
7 a.m.	8
9 a.m.	10
11 a.m.	13
1 p.m.	14
3 p.m.	12
5 p.m.	10

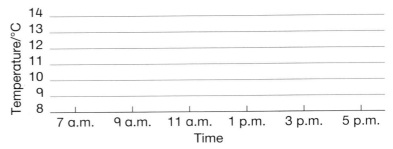

1 Copy the graph on to squared paper. Plot the points and then join them together.

Alf works in a bookshop during the summer holidays. He keeps a record of the number of copies of his favourite book that are sold each week.

Week	Copies sold
1	35
2	30
3	40
4	45
5	25
6	50

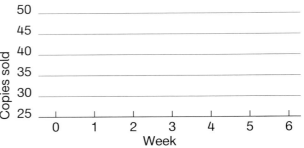

1 Copy the graph on to squared paper. Plot the points and then join them together.

2 Do you think plotting a continuous graph is as useful as drawing a bar chart in this exercise?

In a science lesson, Paulina conducted an experiment. She boiled some water and then measured its temperature every minute as it cooled down. Here are her findings.

Time/minutes	Temperature/°C
1	80
2	64
3	52
4	44
5	41
6	40

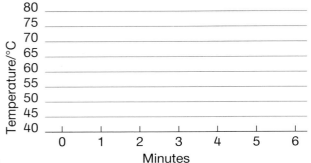

1 Is the water cooling at a steady rate?

Now look back on your work in this lesson.
- What is the difference between the line graphs you have plotted in this lesson and bar charts?
- Explain the difference between exercise D and other exercises.

❷ Reading graphs

These are the publishing presses of a major national daily newspaper. Newspaper staff constantly consider how many copies their paper is selling. Why are the sales of newspaper a good measure for staff to look at?

Fahema and her friends produce a school magazine. The graph shows the number of copies that they sell each week. Look carefully at the graph and then write the answers to these questions.

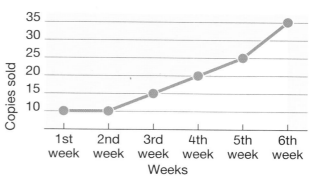

1 In which week did Fahema and her friends sell most copies?
2 In which weeks did they sell fewest copies?
3 In which weeks did they sell the same number of copies?
4 How many more copies did they sell in week 5 than in week 4?
5 How many more copies did they sell in week 6 than in week 1?
6 In what way does the line of the graph between week 5 and week 6 differ from the line in other weeks?

Courtney and his family are going to go to Perugia in Italy for their holiday. Courtney looks at a travel brochure to find out the average temperatures in different months. Look carefully at the graph and then write the answers to these questions.

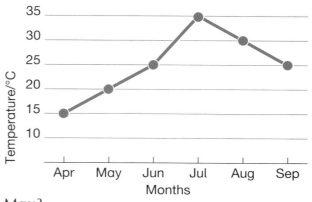

1 What is the average temperature in May?
2 Which month has the warmest average temperature?
3 Which month has the coolest average temperature?
4 Which two months have the same average temperature?
5 Do you think the average temperature in October will be warmer or cooler than in September?
6 How does the line graph show when the greatest rise of temperature happened?

Paul and Sue belong to a theatre group. They keep a record of the size of attendance for each performance. This graph shows the size of audiences in one week. Look at the graph and answer these questions.

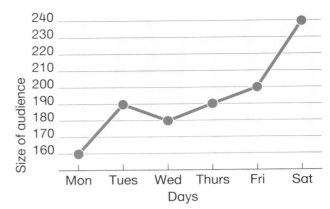

1 How many people watched the play on Tuesday?
2 Which day had the lowest attendance?
3 On which two days did the same number of people attend?
4 How many more people attended on Friday than on Monday?
5 Why do you think more people attended on Saturday than on Monday?
6 Do you think this pattern is likely or not likely to be repeated in other weeks?

Hanif and Jason go on a cycling holiday in France. They keep a record of how far they travel each day. They avoid busy towns and ride on country and mountain routes. This is shown on the graph. Look at the graph and answer these questions.

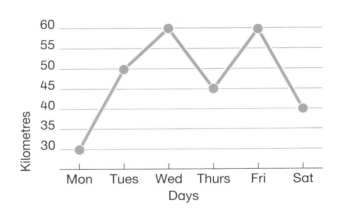

1 How far did they travel on Tuesday?
2 How much further did they travel on Wednesday than on Monday?
3 How far did they travel on Saturday?
4 When they travel less distance, are they in hilly country or in flat country?
5 Were they climbing a mountain or going down a mountain on Wednesday?
6 In what way is the shape of the graph confusing?

Now look back on your work in this lesson.
• In what way is the work on line graphs more than just work with co-ordinates?
• How can a line graph be confusing if you do not read it carefully?

③ Overall shape of graphs

This Christmas tree is outside the White House in Washington D.C.
Do you have a Christmas tree at home?
How long before Christmas do people normally buy Christmas trees?

Trevor helps to prepare Christmas trees for sale. He prepares them in batches of 10, and keeps a record of the number of trees sold as Christmas approaches. Here are his findings. Look at this graph and answers these questions.

1 In which week were the fewest Christmas trees sold?
2 In which week were the most Christmas trees sold?
3 In which two weeks were the same number of Christmas trees sold?
4 How many Christmas trees were sold altogether in the time that Trevor kept his record?
5 How many more Christmas trees were sold in the week starting 21 December than in the week starting 14 December?
6 What can you say about the sale of Christmas trees generally?

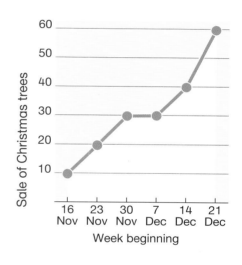

John has five older brothers. The ages and heights of all of the boys are shown on this graph. Write the answers to these questions.

1 Who is the shortest brother?
2 Who is the tallest brother?
3 How much taller is Tony than Simon?
4 How much taller is Colin than Frank?
5 How much taller is Steve than John?
6 What do you notice about the ages and heights of the brothers generally?

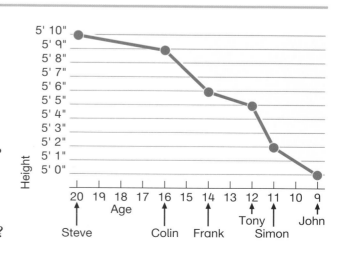

Rushna works at her local swimming pool. She kept a record of the number of people that used the swimming pool during a week in July to the nearest 10. She also kept a record of the temperature outside at noon on each of the days. Look at this graph and answer these questions.

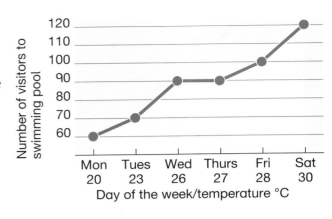

1 On which day did most people visit the swimming pool?
2 On which day did the fewest people visit the swimming pool?
3 How many more people visited on Wednesday than on Monday?
4 How many more people visited on Friday than on Tuesday?
5 On which two days did the same number of people visit?
6 Do you think there is a link between the temperature of the day and the number of people that went swimming? If *yes*, explain what it is.

Rita works in the music section of the library during the holidays. She keeps a record of how many CDs she sells each week to nearest ten. Look at this graph and answer these questions.

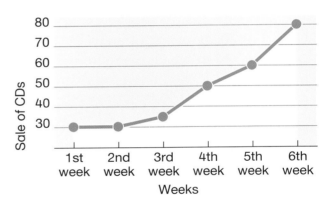

1 In which week were most CDs sold?
2 In which weeks were the fewest CDs sold?
3 How many more CDs were sold in the fifth week than in the fourth week?
4 How many more CDs were sold in the sixth week than in the first week?
5 What can you say about the sale of the CDs generally?
6 About how many CDs would you expect to be sold in the seventh week? Give your reasons.

Now look back on your work in this lesson.
- Do graphs of things that happen with time always have the same pattern of rising?
- What can you tell by looking at the general shape of a graph rather than the separate points?

④ Devise a bar chart

Motor racing is a popular sport to watch.
But why don't more people see it live rather than on TV?

Each pupil in one class was asked to choose their favourite sport.
Here is what was found.

Favourite sport	Number of pupils
Football	10
Hockey	4
Cricket	6
Tennis	4
Motor racing	8
Snooker	2

1 Show these results as a bar chart.

2 There is an offer of free tickets for the whole class for the two most popular sports (not including motor racing). Which two sports these will be?

Jason carried out a survey of his class to find out how they travelled to school.

Way of travelling	Number of pupils
Walk	5
Car	10
Bike	5
Bus	6
Train	2
Tram	2

1 Construct a bar chart to show Jason's data.

Most of the pupils in Sandra's class like music, but they have very different musical tastes. Sandra carries out a questionnaire in order to find out which types of music are most popular.

Type of music	Number of pupils
Heavy metal	3
Hip hop	6
Jazz	2
Classical	4
Rap	8
House	4

1 Construct a bar chart using her data.

Helen conducts a survey to find out her friends' favourite colour.

Favourite colour	Number of pupils
Red	10
Blue	6
Green	4
Purple	3
Orange	2
Yellow	5

1 Construct a bar chart using her data.

Winston's neighbour runs a café. He held a survey to see which drinks had the highest sales.

Type of drink	Number sold
Coffee	20
Tea	8
Hot chocolate	15
Cola	35
Orange	10
Blackcurrant	5

1 Construct a bar chart using his data.

Now look back on your work in this lesson.
- How do you decide on the markers on the vertical number line for a bar chart?
- Why do you think many people prefer bar charts to lists of numbers?

⑤ Even chances

This is a football match played between Arsenal and Everton. Who do you think will win? Does everyone agree on that? When teams are roughly of the same strengths we say their chances of either team winning are called *even*.

What if one team is playing with only nine players because of injuries or send-offs? Then the chances will be *worse than even* for that team, and *better than even* for the other team.

Imagine you are watching this match. Everton is playing with only 9 players and Arsenal with the full 11 players.
Use *even, better than even,* and *worse than even* to call these chances. Remember, this is a mathematical question, not a 'supporting and hoping' question!

1 The next player to touch the ball is wearing a red shirt.
2 The next player to score a goal is wearing a white shirt.
3 The next player to touch the ball is wearing a blue shirt.
4 The next player to score a goal is an Arsenal player.
5 The next player to touch the ball is wearing blue shorts.

In each question below, the six numbers are written on the six sides of a dice. The dice is thrown once.

1 7, 9, 12, 7, 15, 7

Is it an even chance or not that 7 will be thrown?

2 16, 14, 16, 18, 16, 16

Is it an even chance or not that 16 will be thrown?

3 5, 15, 5, 25, 18, 35

Is it an even chance or not that 5 will be thrown?

4 100, 200, 150, 200, 200, 600

Is it an even chance or not that 200 will be thrown?

5 30, 40, 30, 30, 30, 60

Is it an even chance or not that 30 will be thrown?

6 11, 55, 11, 44, 11, 22

Is it an even chance or not that 11 will be thrown?

At the end of a visit to a sweet factory, you are asked to play a game. First you have to look at different trays, each loaded with two or more types of sweets or biscuits. Then you write one choice from each tray on a piece of paper.

Now you put on a blindfold and pick one sweet from each tray. If you choose the same sweet that you wrote down, you will be given a huge box of it to take home. Otherwise you get nothing!

Remember, you are making your choice so you can take home as much as possible, not because you like or dislike something!

Tray	My choice	Even chance	Better than evens	Worse than evens

1 Copy the table and complete it with the best choices possible. Place a tick to show how lucky you think you'll be in one of the columns next to each of your choices.

Imagine these words are cut up and the letters put in a hat. Your answer to each question needs to show whether you think there is an even chance, a better than even chance or a worse than even chance.

1 A N N A – What is the chance of drawing an A?
2 B U B B L E S – What is the chance of drawing a B?
3 C O O L – What is the chance of drawing an O?
4 S E T T L E R S – What is the chance of drawing a T?
5 B O B B Y – What is the chance of drawing a B?
6 S E S S I O N S – What is the chance of drawing an S?

Look back at your work in this lesson.
- What other words or phrases can you use that mean *evens*?
- Can you tell if something has a *better than evens* or a *worse than evens* chance?

⑥ Skills in graphs

The photograph shows a busy farm.
School visits to city farms are increasingly popular.
Why do you think is that?

Jason's older brother works on a city farm.
He keeps a record of the number of school
visits made to the farm each month.
Look at Jason's record for January to June.
Copy the graph on to squared paper and
then plot the points and join them together.

Month	School visits
January	10
February	10
March	15
April	20
May	30
June	40

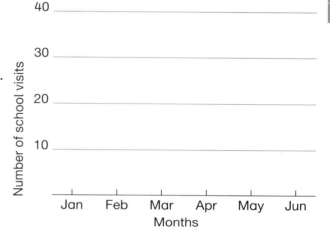

Pauline and her family are going to go to
Sardinia for their holiday. Pauline looks at
a travel brochure to find out the average
temperature in different months. These are
shown in this graph. Look at the graph and
answer these questions.

1 What is the average temperature in June?
2 Which two months have the hottest average
temperatures?
3 Which month has the coolest average
temperature?
4 Which two months have the same average
temperatures?
5 How much warmer is the average
temperature in July than in May?
6 Do you think the average temperature in
March will be warmer or cooler than in
June?

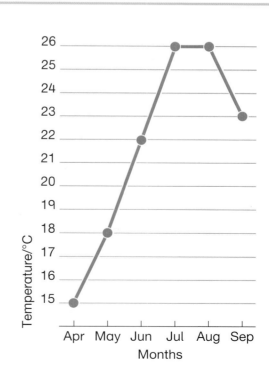

Desmond helps his dad in the shop during the run-up to Christmas.
He keeps a record of the number of boxes of Christmas cards that they sell.
Look at the graph and then answer these questions.

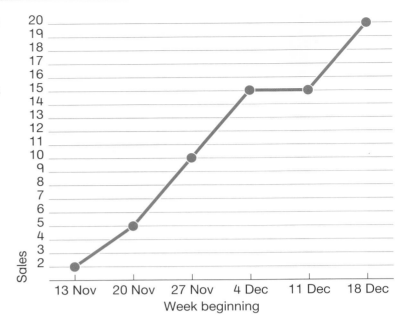

1 In which week were the fewest boxes sold?
2 How many more boxes were sold in the week starting 20th November than in the week starting 13th November?
3 In which two weeks were the same number of boxes sold?
4 Do you think they will sell more boxes in the week starting 1st January than they did in the week starting 18th December?
5 Were more boxes sold in the week starting 20th November than in the week starting 4th December?
6 What do you notice about the sale of the Christmas cards generally?

Hanif wants to find out which Premiership football club is the most popular with his class. Each member of the class can only vote for one team and Hanif records each vote. Look at his data and then construct a bar chart.

Team	Votes
Arsenal	6
Manchester United	8
Chelsea	8
Liverpool	5
Newcastle	2
Aston Villa	3

Now look back on your work in this lesson.
• Think of any new words you have learnt in this module.
• How can you predict what a graph will look like before you draw it?

Number and algebra

❶ Sets of 10s and 100s
Finding how many sets of 10s and 100s there are in a three-digit number. Multiplying and dividing by 10 and 100

❷ Rounding or cutting off
Measuring to the nearest whole unit, either by ignoring anything less than a whole unit, or by rounding it up to a whole

❸ Reading tenths in scales
Knowing how to read to the nearest tenth; writing this with the decimal point when the scale is marked but not numbered

❹ How many sevens in 70?
Calculating how many sets of 10 there are in a 10s number

❺ Number counters
Reading counters which use zeros at the front of whole numbers, and understanding that this does not affect the value

❻ Number and algebra skills
Practising skills in tenths, 10s, 100s, number counters and rounding off numbers

Key words and phrases

decimals
divisions between unit markers on a scale
factor
fraction
multiples and packs of 10s and 100s
place value
slots (or cells) in counters
tenths

approximate
closest to
correct to the nearest
cutting off
nearest
rounding
truncating

① Sets of 10s and 100s

The cheapest housing is in blocks of flats. If the smaller blocks of flats in this housing estate have 10 flats, how many blocks are needed for 80 flats? and for 150 flats?If the largest blocks have 100 flats each, how many blocks are needed for 1200 flats?

Work out these multiplication sums to find the number in the box.

1 10 × ☐ = 40

2 ☐ × 8 = 80

3 10 × ☐ 12 = ☐

4 10 × ☐ 24 = ☐

5 7 × ☐ = 70

6 15 × ☐ 10 = ☐

7 36 × ☐ 10 = ☐

8 62 × ☐ = 6200

Now do these divisions.

9 90 ÷ 10 = ☐

10 50 ÷ ☐ = 5

11 150 ÷ 10 = ☐

12 ☐ ÷ 10 = 25

How many 10s are there in these?

13 440

14 230

15 870

16 390

1 Multiply the following numbers by 100.

a 4   d 35

b 7   e 52

c 12   f 63

2 Divide these numbers by 100.

a 500   d 3700

b 800   e 8600

c 1200   f 7900

These Christmas crackers come in boxes of 10.

How many crackers would you get if you bought:

1 2 boxes

2 5 boxes

3 11 boxes

4 20 boxes

5 Anisha is arranging a party for 150 children. How many boxes will she need to buy?

Josh collects 5p coins in a jar.

1 He has saved 50p. How many coins are in his jar?

2 When he has 30 coins how much will he have?

3 If he saves 50p a week, how many weeks will it be before he has £50?

Now solve these problems.

1 Pupils sold 564 raffle tickets at the school fête. If the tickets were in books of 100 how many books of tickets were used?

2 At the Win a Teddy stall 350 tickets were sold. Tickets here were priced at 10 for £2. How much money was made on this stall?

3 The refreshment stall sold 127 cups of tea. If the teapot holds 10 cups of tea, how many times did it need filling during the day?

Now look back on your work in this lesson.

- Are you confident when multiplying and dividing by 100?
- Can you see how this can be useful when changing centimetres to metres?

② Rounding or cutting off

The gardener has experimented with three types of plant feed to see which allows better growth. She has measured the plants in centimetres and written their measurements in decimals.

Some people just leave off anything which is less than one centimetre. This is called *cutting off*. Other people ignore the fraction if it is less than half, but take anything more than half as a whole one. This called *rounding*.

Which method do you prefer? Why?

For each of the plant measurements you can see in the picture above, write down the cut-off measurement, then the rounded measurement to the nearest centimetre.
Copy and complete this table.

Plant	Full measurement	Cut-off measurement	Rounded measurement
A	⊚	⊚	⊚
B	⊚	⊚	⊚
C	⊚	⊚	⊚
D	⊚	⊚	⊚
E	⊚	⊚	⊚
F	⊚	⊚	⊚
G	⊚	⊚	⊚

Session measures his table. It measures 105.6 cm by 53.1 cm.
1. Write both these measurements correct to the nearest whole centimetre.
2. Using the results you found, what do you notice about the length and width of his table?

C

Can you solve these?

1 Carly is 162.3 cm tall. How many millimetres must she grow before she can say that she is 163 cm to the nearest whole centimetre?

2 James now measures 172 cm to the nearest centimetre. When he was measured last term, he was 171.4 cm exactly. Has James grown?

3 How do you know?

4 Piers was also measured again this term. His height is 170 cm to the nearest centimetre. Last term his height was exactly 169.6 cm. Has Piers grown?

5 Give a reason for your answer.

D

Now solve these.

1 Mr Roberts knows that his Maths room is 7.3 metres long. He gets Sonas to measure it roughly using a metre trundle wheel. How many times should the trundle wheel click along the length of the room?

2 In the primary school the younger children use a ruler that has only centimetres marked on it. They have to measure items to the nearest centimetre. What should they write if their Maths books measure 29.7 cm by 16.2 cm?

3 Jenny's new home is 5.7 km from the nearest large town, 10.4 km from the coast and 3.8 km from her school. She writes to her grandparents to tell them about it and decides to give the distances to the nearest kilometre. What should she write?

E

Sparks and Mensers are having a sale. They decide to reduce some garments by half and then give the price to the nearest whole pound. Write down the sale price of these coats.

Now look back on your work in this lesson.
- When is it necessary to give measurements very accurately?
- When is it sufficient to give measurements to the nearest whole number?

③ Reading tenths in scales

Weight is measured in kilograms today. Things are unlikely to weigh an exact number of kilograms so there could be 10 divisions in between each kilogram mark. How many grams would each division represent? How much does the penguin weigh to the nearest kilogram?

A Four items have been measured.

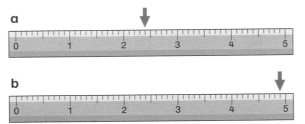

a

c

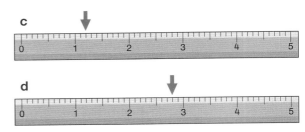

b

d

1 Write down the measurements that are shown on these rulers.

B Use a ruler that is marked in centimetres and millimetres to measure these things, correct to one decimal place.
1 The length of your pen
2 The length of your pencil
3 The length of your exercise book
4 The width of the picture at the top of this page

C These are the flood levels reached by Amanda's local river in the years that are marked on the flood board.

1 How high did the water rise in 1984?
2 How high did it rise after that?
3 How much difference was there in the level in 1969 and 1947?
4 In 1975 how much more would the river have had to rise for the flood level to be 2 m?
5 If the flood level is more than 2 m, the houses by the river are flooded. How many times has this happened since 1947?

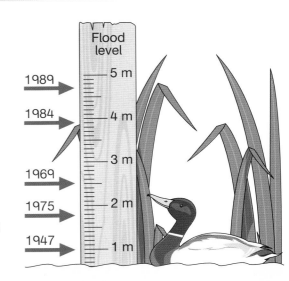

The large numbers on these weighing scales show kilograms.

1 Write down the weights shown on each dial giving your answer to one decimal place of a kilogram.

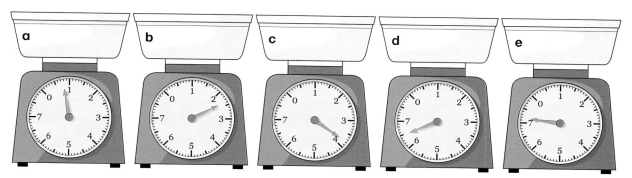

Work with three friends. Use the bathroom scales to weigh each person's schoolbag in kilograms with one decimal place.
1 Write down the weight of each schoolbag.
2 Were any of the bags an exact number of kilograms?

Several years ago a row of trees was planted in the park. Some have grown more than others.

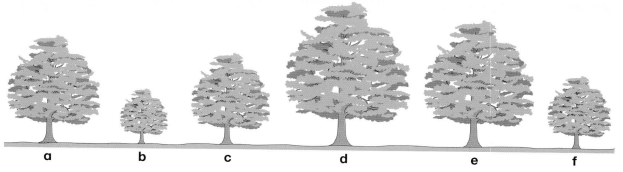

1 If 1 cm in the picture represents 1 metre, give the measurements of the trees in centimetres and write down your results.
2 How high is the tallest tree?
3 Which tree is the shortest?
4 How much taller than tree **e** is tree **d**?
5 How much will tree **b** have to grow to be as tall as tree **a**?
6 Which tree is taller than tree **c** and shorter than tree **e**?

Now look back on your work in this lesson.
- Can you use one decimal place if there are 10 divisions on the scale?
- Can you use the decimal place if there are less or more divisions than 10?

④ How many sevens in 70?

The amount of red carpet needed depends on how far a VIP has to walk – and maybe how famous they are!

 Work out the answers to these problems.

1. A roll in the local carpet shop contains 80 m of carpet. Each flat on the estate needs 8 m of this carpet. How many flats can be fitted from the roll?
2. Each bathroom needs 2 m of bathroom carpet. How many metres of carpet are needed to fit the same number of flats as in question 1?
3. A roll of 70 m is needed to cover a number of rooms. Each room needs 7 m. How many rooms can be covered?
4. A roll of 65 metres is used to cover six rooms of the same size. Roughly how much carpet will each room take?
5. Half of a roll of 80 metres is used to cover ten hallways fully. How much did each hallway need?

 Can you solve these?

1. $90/9 = \boxed{}$
2. $30/\boxed{} = 10$
3. $70/7 = \boxed{}$
4. $50 \div \boxed{} = 10$
5. $\boxed{} \div 2 = 10$
6. $100 \div 10 = \boxed{}$
7. $\boxed{}$ divided in 3s is 10
8. 40 divided in $\boxed{}$ equals 4
9. 100 divided in $\boxed{}$ makes 10
10. 10 divided in $\boxed{}$ makes 10

C Now solve these.

1 How many 4s are there in 40?

2 How many 8s are there in 80?

3 How many 6s are there in 60?

Use your answers to find these out.

4 How many 8s in 40?

5 How many 4s in 80?

6 How many 3s in 60?

7 How many 4s in 60?

D Now find the answers to these.

1 How many 2p coins do you need to exchange for a 20p coin?

2 Jan is saving 5p coins. How many will she need before she has 50p?

3 How many 10p coins make £1?

4 How many 20p coins make £2?

5 How many 50p coins make £5?

6 You have lots of 20p coins and seven 2p coins. How can you make £1.50 exactly?

E Work these out.

1 Tom and Sahir have 90p to spend. They buy a card for 30p. They spend the rest of their money on 6p chews. How many chews do they get each?

2 Dan has 75p. How many 7p stickers can he buy? Will he have any money left? How much?

F Now solve these.

1 Four schools join together for Sports Day. Main Road School sends 40 pupils, St John's School sends 20 pupils, Cross High School sends 15 pupils and Friars' Heath School sends 25 pupils. How many teams of 10 can be made from all the pupils from these four schools?

2 If four of the teams are entered for the 100 m race and 10 competitors are in each heat, how many heats will there be?

Now look back on your work in this lesson.
- Why is it easier to use multiples of 10 than other multiples in solving number problems?
- What other multiples can you easily use apart from multiples of 10?

⑤ Number counters

What will be the reading on the mileometer of a brand new car?
It may have done several miles around the factory and showroom while being tested and moved. Don't expect all zeros!

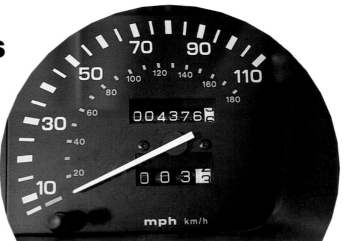

 Mr Green owns a second-hand car business. Here are the readings on the mileometers of six of the cars he has for sale. How many miles had each of these cars done when he bought them?

1

3

5

2

4

6
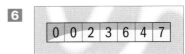

 The new car that John's dad bought from a showroom had already done 20 miles when they went to pick it up. The mileometer had six spaces for the figures.

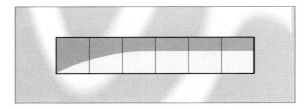

1 Show what the figures on the mileometer looked like when John's dad bought it.

2 John lives 15 miles from the showroom. What did the mileometer say when they got home?

John's family decided to go to the sea for a trip in the new car. His dad drove 52 miles to the coast. His mum drove back by a different route and travelled 54 miles.

3 Show the reading on the mileometer when they arrived at the sea.

4 Give the final reading when they got back home again.

The reading on the meter of the school photocopier is:

1 How many copies have been made so far?
2 Mrs Myers makes 30 copies of a worksheet for her class. What does the meter say now?
3 Mr Kahn uses the machine after Mrs Myers. When he finishes the reading is:

How many copies has he made?

Last month Sanjay's electricity meter read:

The month before it had read:

1 How many units had he used between the readings?
2 If he uses 180 units this month what will be the new reading on the meter?

Farah has a counter on her computer game that shows the score she has got.
Here are her scores for five games that she played last night.

1 In which game was her score the worst?
2 In which two games were her scores nearest?
3 How many more points did she score in game 2 than game 4?
4 Which was her best game?

Now look back on your work in this lesson.
• Do you know how to read a number from a counter that has 0000 at the front?
• Why is it useful to use zeros in front in counters?

⑥ Number and algebra skills

Do you know how many flowers you will get in a bunch? It is often 10 stems. You can easily work out how many bunches to buy if you know how many flowers are needed.

A

Melissa and her mum are making flower arrangements to go on the dining tables at a wedding reception.

There are 20 tables and they need to put a flower arrangement on each table. The florist sells all his flowers in bunches of 10.

1. They want to put three roses in each arrangement. How many roses will they need?
2. How many bunches of roses should they buy?
3. They also need four carnations for each arrangement. How many carnations will they need?
4. How many bunches of carnations should they buy?
5. They want a spray of gypsophilia for each vase. This is sold at 50p a spray. How much will the gypsophilia cost them?

B

Work out these problems.

1. Robert is 176.7 cm tall. How tall is he to the nearest centimetre?
2. The drive to Graham's favourite picnic area is 4.3 miles. He decides to walk there with his friends. They are able to take a shortcut for a small part of the journey by walking along a footpath to the tables.
   a. About how far is the walk?
   b. Graham's dad drives there with the picnic. Give the length of the drive there and back, correct to the nearest whole number of miles.

C

Get these objects from your teacher. Measure the length of each one, using a centimetre ruler with the divisions in millimetres.

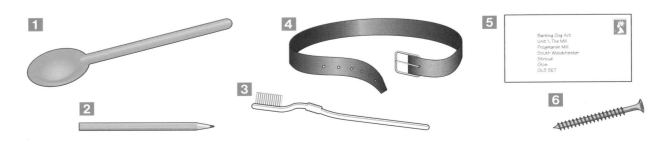

Now work these out.

1 There are 70 primary school children going to a pantomime. They are divided into groups of seven children. Each group will have one teacher. How many teachers will need to go with them?

2 Lee had nine goes on the tombola at the fête. He was given 10p change from £1. What was the cost of one go?

3 Kim bought a box of 10 drinking glasses at a car boot sale for £1.80. What did she pay for each glass?

Mr Talbot's class were in charge of counting how many people came to the open day at their school. They took it in turns to sit by the door and click the counter as visitors came in. Use a calculator to work out the number of visitors.

1 When John finished his turn the counter read:

How many visitors had come in?

2 Jane finished the next turn with the counter reading:

How many visitors had arrived altogether by then?

3 How many came during Jane's turn?

4 After the last visitor had arrived the final reading on the counter was:

How many visitors came to the open day?

5 How many of them arrived after Jane had finished her turn?

Write all these numbers correct to the nearest whole number.

1 45.7 **3** 32.9 **5** 87.1 **7** 64.3

2 21.8 **4** 90.7 **6** 104.2 **8** 999.9

Now look back on your work in this lesson.
- How do you know when to divide and when to multiply to solve a problem written in words?
- How do you round decimal numbers to the nearest whole number?

Module ❶4

Shape and space

❶ Describing 3D shapes
Naming and drawing 3D shapes

❷ Making 3D shape models
Recognising 3D shapes in everyday life, and making models of them

❸ Drawing rectangles to measure
Drawing rectangles and squares using measurements of the length of sides

❹ All the way round
Measuring the perimeter of shapes; calculating the perimeters of regular ones when not all the sides are given

❺ Four directions
Knowing which is north, east, south and west on maps; giving instructions using these directions

❻ Shape and space skills
Practising the skills learnt about 3D objects, perimeters and directions

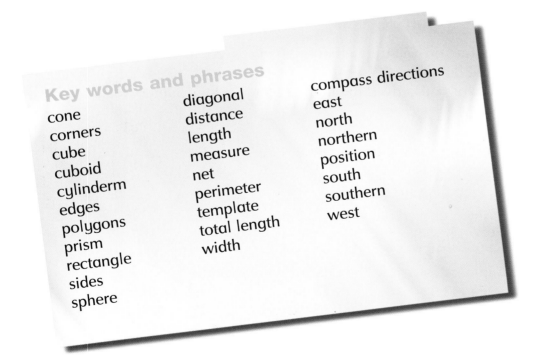

Key words and phrases

cone
corners
cube
cuboid
cylinderm
edges
polygons
prism
rectangle
sides
sphere

diagonal
distance
length
measure
net
perimeter
template
total length
width

compass directions
east
north
northern
position
south
southern
west

① Describing 3D shapes

This is one of the great pyramids of Giza in Egypt. The biggest pyramid was the World's tallest building for over 4000 years, and it was built with over 2 million cuboid blocks of stone. You can see the edges and corners of the blocks now, but when this was built it would have been covered in granite and the edges would have been smooth.

 Copy this square.

1. Label all the sides with the word *side*. How do you know they are the same length?
2. Label the corners clockwise. Write **c1** for the first corner at the bottom left. Label the top left corner **c2**, the top right corner **c3**, and the bottom right corner **c4**.
3. Write the word *face* on the square, showing there is only one square in the shape.

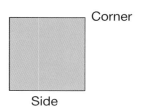

Now you are going to make this square into a cube. Copy the square on a separate piece of paper. Cut it out and place it on top and to the side of the first square, as shown here. Now draw around it and copy the labels.

4. How many corners you can see now?

Now use your ruler to join corner **c1** on the back square to corner **c1** in the front square. Repeat this with corner **c2** and corner **c4**. You have to imagine what should happen to corner **c3**.

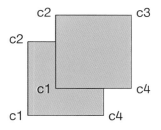

You have now constructed a cube. Look at your set of solid shapes. Find a cube and count the faces, the corners and the sides.

5. How many square faces does a cube have?
6. How many sides?
7. How many corners?
8. What can help to make your picture of the cube clearer or better?

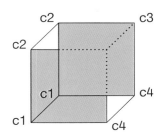

Copy the square in exercise A again.

Now slide the square 1 cm to the left and 1 cm down the page.

Draw round the square in its new position. Label the corners in the same way as exercise A.

Join the corners that have the same labels. Copy and complete these sentences choosing one of the words from the word box to fill the blanks.

eight	same	twelve	four	one	six	square

1 The square has ____ sides, ____ corners, and ____ face.

2 A cube has ____ corners.

3 A cube has ____ faces. Each of them is a _____ shape.

4 A cube has ____ edges, all of the _____ length.

Copy this rectangle and complete the sentences in each question.

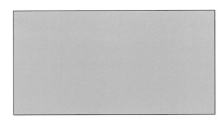

1 A rectangle has ____ sides. It has ____ long sides, and ____ shorter sides.

2 A rectangle has ____ corners.

3 The rectangle has ____ faces.

You can now repeat the exercises A and B to form a cuboid, which should look like this:

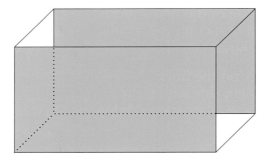

Complete these sentences.

4 A cuboid has ____ corners.

5 A cuboid has ____ faces. There are ____ bigger faces which are the same size, and ____ smaller faces.

6 A cuboid has ____ edges.

Now think about diagonals.

> A straight line that joins opposite corners in a shape is called a diagonal line.

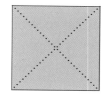
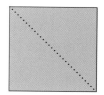

1 How many diagonals can be drawn on a square shape on the page?

2 Why is it true that on a square the number of diagonals is half the number of corners?

3 Now look at a cube. How many diagonals does a solid cube have on all its faces?

4 Why are there more diagonals on a solid cube than half the number of its corners?

5 Look at a solid cuboid, complete this sentence.
A cuboid has ____ faces, ____ diagonals, and ____ corners.

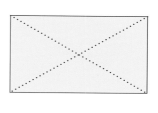

6 Is there a difference in the number of faces between a cube and a cuboid?

7 In the number of corners?

8 In the number of diagonals?

9 In the number of sides?

10 What is the real difference between the cube and the cuboid?

Copy this triangle and label it as shown.

1 How many sides are there?

2 How many corners?

3 How many faces?

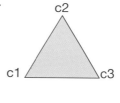

Now slide the triangle to the right, up the page. Draw the shape again.

4 How many corners can you see now?

5 Join the corners to construct a prism.

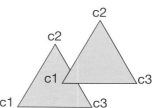

Look at your solid shapes and find a prism.

6 How many triangular faces can you see?

7 How many rectangular faces can you see?

8 Are the rectangles all the same size?

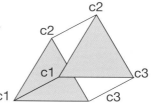

Now look back on your work in this lesson.
- What mathematical features can you use to describe solid shapes?
- What is the difference between a cube and a cuboid?

2 Making 3D shape models

In space there are often regular shapes, such as spheres and cylinders.
How do you describe in words the difference between spheres and cylinders?

Look at these shapes.

cuboid

cube

sphere

cylinder

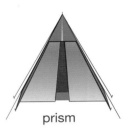
prism

pyramid

Make a list of other things of the same shape.
1 Three things that are in the shape of a cube
2 Three things that look like a sphere
3 Three cuboids
4 Three cylinders
5 Look around the classroom and list any shapes that are different from the shapes above.

When this cube is cut open at some of the edges it makes a *net* of six squares connected in the shape of a cross.

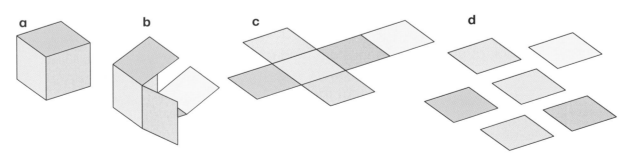

a   b   c   d

Look at this view of the cube above.
1 What colour is the bottom face of the cube?
2 What colour is the back face?
3 What colour is the right-hand side of the cube?

1 Test yourself. Follow these steps.

a Draw the cross shape of six squares first, using a square as a template.

b Cut out the net with scissors.

c Fold the shape in the right way to make a cube.

2 Cuboids come in many different shapes and sizes. Look at the ones here, and describe the faces on the cuboids.

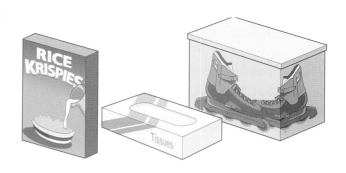

3 Sketch in your book all the faces you would be able to see on the tissue box, like this:

4 Which face of the tissue box did each of the rectangles **a, b, c, d, e,** and **f** come from?

Choose from the following: top, bottom, left-hand side, right-hand side, front and back.

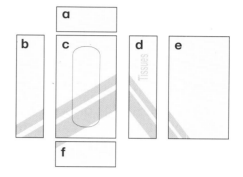

Look back at the pictures in exercise A.

Here are faces from some of the shapes when they are split up.

Which faces form which of the solid shapes? Use the words in the box to help you.

cone   cube   square-based pyramid   prism
triangular-based pyramid   cylinder   cuboid

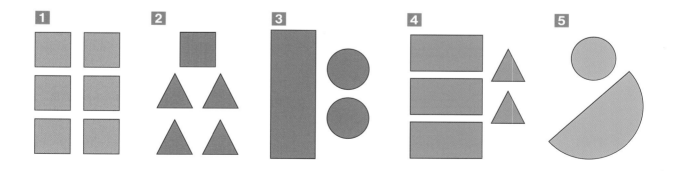

Now look back on your work in this lesson.

- Can you picture in your mind how a cube box is made of six square faces?
- Name some regular 3D shapes that you see around you.

③ Drawing rectangles to measure

Why is it easier to make mosaics in square and rectangular tiles? Are these two statements true for a rectangle?
- The pairs of opposite sides must be parallel to each other.
- The four corners of a rectangle must be right angles.

Do the two statements apply to a square? Is a square a kind of rectangle?

Measure the sides of your Maths Direct textbook. Answer these questions to the nearest centimetre.
1. What is the measurement of the longer sides?
2. What is the measurement of the shorter sides?
3. Using these measurements, draw a rectangle of half the size.

Ask your teacher for a square of card or a set square. You could also use the corner of a book to make sure the angle is exactly 90° (a right angle).
4. Now draw a rectangle measuring 8 cm × 4 cm, using your square corner to help you to get the lines at right angles to each other.

These grids show two sides of a rectangle.

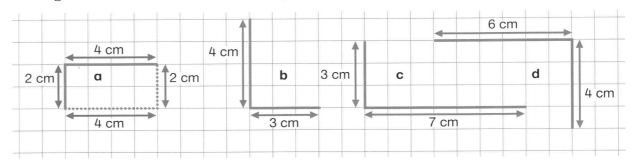

1. Using squared paper, copy the lines and complete each grid to form a rectangle. The first one is done for you.

Using squared paper, draw these rectangles.
1. length 5 cm × width 3 cm
2. length 4 cm × width 1 cm
3. length 8 cm × width 4 cm
4. length 6 cm × width 2 cm
5. length 7 cm × width 4 cm
6. length 6 cm × width 3 cm

Look at these rectangles to answer the questions.

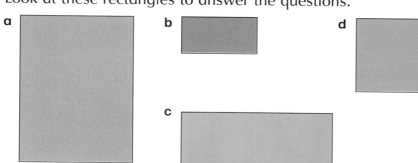

Rectangle	Length (cm)	Width (cm)
a	✿	✿
b	✿	✿
c	✿	✿
d	✿	✿
e	✿	✿
f	✿	✿

1 Measure the sides of these shapes and record your measurements on this table.

2 How many shapes are rectangles?

3 What is the name of the other two shapes that you have drawn?

Complete the following rectangles using your square corner.

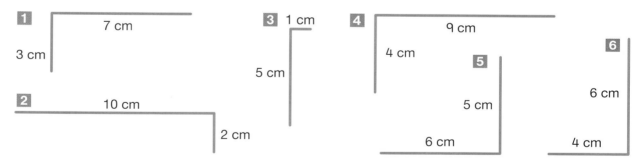

1 7 cm, 3 cm

2 10 cm, 2 cm

3 1 cm, 5 cm

4 9 cm, 4 cm

5 5 cm, 6 cm

6 6 cm, 4 cm

Draw these shapes and label them square or rectangle.

1 length 7 cm × width 2 cm

2 length 3 cm × width 1 cm

3 length 6 cm × width 6 cm

4 length 4 cm × width 2 cm

5 length 4 cm × width 4 cm

6 length 8 cm × width 7 cm

Now look back on your work in this lesson.
* What is the smallest measurement you need to draw a rectangle?
* Is there a real difference between a rectangle and a square?

④ All the way round

The owner of this castle can tell at a glance how far his land extends. A surrounding edge is called a *perimeter*, a measure of border length.

Ask your teacher for a set of regular polygons.

1. Draw round each shape.
2. Measure the lengths of every side of each shape.
3. Add the lengths of the sides together for each shape. This will give you the total distance around the outside edge of the shapes. We call this the perimeter of the shape.
4. Find the perimeter of a square that has sides of 4 cm.
5. Find the perimeter of a rectangle that has a length of 5 cm and a width of 4 cm.
6. Find the lengths of the sides of a square that has a perimeter of 24 cm. Remember all sides of a square are equal lengths.

Copy and complete the perimeters of these pictures.

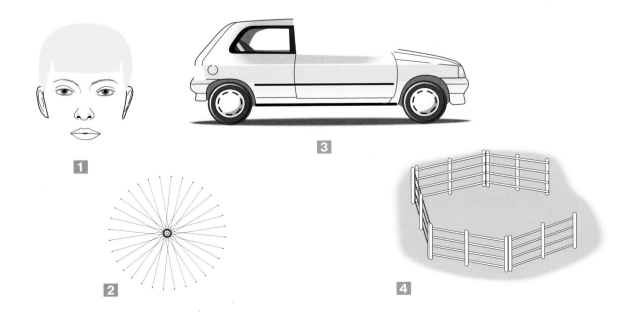

1

2

3

4

C

To find out the perimeter of a shape you add together all of the sides.

10 cm

2 cm   2 cm

10 cm

10 + 2 + 10 + 2 = 24 cm
The perimeter of this rectangle is 24 centimetres.

Find the distance around the perimeters of the shapes below.

1
5 cm
5 cm   20 CM   5 cm
5 cm

3
3 cm   3 cm
3 cm

6
4 cm
5½ cm
3 cm   2 cm
3 cm   1 cm

7
2 cm   2 cm
3 cm   3 cm

4
3 cm
3 cm   3 cm
3 cm

2
7 cm
3 cm   3 cm
7 cm

5 5 cm
3 cm
4 cm

8 8 cm
2 cm
8 cm
2 cm

Measure the perimeter of the following items.

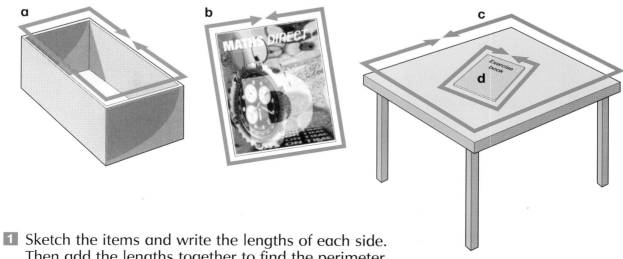

a

b

MATHS DIRECT

c

Exercise book

d

1 Sketch the items and write the lengths of each side.
Then add the lengths together to find the perimeter.

Find the lengths of the missing sides of these shapes.
Clue: add the sides you have been given together, then subtract
your answer from the total perimeter.

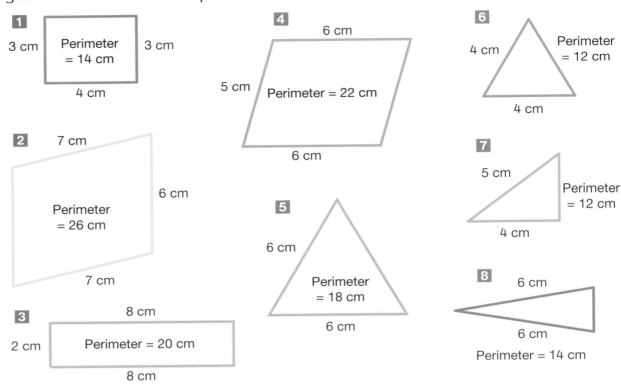

1

3 cm | Perimeter = 14 cm | 3 cm
4 cm

2

7 cm

Perimeter = 26 cm

6 cm

7 cm

3

2 cm | Perimeter = 20 cm
8 cm
8 cm

4

6 cm
5 cm | Perimeter = 22 cm
6 cm

5

6 cm
Perimeter = 18 cm
6 cm

6

4 cm | Perimeter = 12 cm
4 cm

7

5 cm | Perimeter = 12 cm
4 cm

8

6 cm
6 cm
Perimeter = 14 cm

Measure the lengths of the sides of these shapes and find their
perimeter to the nearest centimetre.

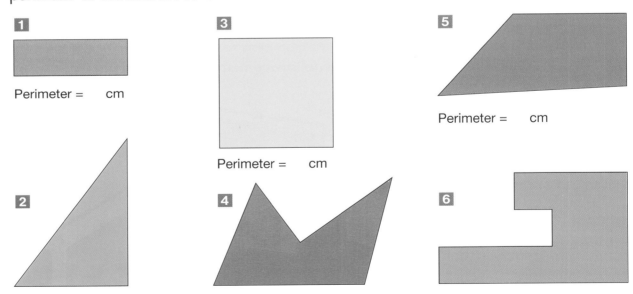

1

Perimeter =   cm

2

3

Perimeter =   cm

4

5

Perimeter =   cm

6

Now look back on your work in this lesson.
- What is the difference between perimeter and the area of a shape?
- What is an easy way of finding the perimeter of any rectangle?

⑤ Four directions

This is the sun setting in the west. If you were looking directly at it, which direction would north be? Some people use sayings to help them remember the positions of the four compass points clockwise.
Which way of remembering the compass directions do you prefer?

Trace the compass cross on to a small piece of tracing paper.

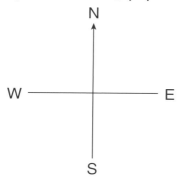

Look at the map and then complete these sentences. Using your traced compass to help you, give compass points for your answers.

1 Cambridge is _____ of London.
2 London is to the _____ of Reading.
3 Salisbury is _____ of Reading.
4 Brighton is to the _____ of Folkestone.
5 Salisbury is _____ of Yeovil.
6 Sheffield is _____ of Luton.

Look at the map in exercise A and name these towns.
1 It is west of Cambridge.
2 It is north of Felixstowe.
3 It is east of London.
4 It is north of Gloucester.
5 It is south of Chester.
6 It is west of Felixstowe.

You are going on a touring holiday around the south of England. Write the directions you need to travel through the following places. Use compass directions to help you.

Start in central London. Go _____ to Margate, _____ to Folkestone, _____ to Brighton, _____ to Salisbury, _____ to Reading, _____ to Bristol, _____ to Gloucester, _____ to Cambridge, and then back to London.

Look at the world map.

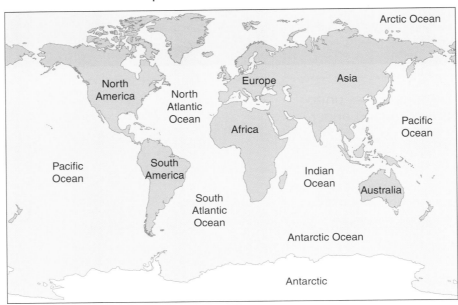

Find the British Isles. Place the compass cross on the centre of the British Isles. List any oceans you can see.

1 To the north of the British Isles   **3** To the south
2 To the east   **4** To the west

Copy and complete these sentences.

5 Asia is to the _____ of the Indian ocean.
6 The North Atlantic Ocean is to the _____ of Europe.
7 South America is to the _____ of the Pacific Ocean, and to the west of the _____ _____ Ocean.
8 Australia is to the _____ of the Pacific Ocean.
9 Describe the position of North America.
10 Name the oceans to the east and to the west of Africa.

Now look back on your work in this lesson.
- Can a place be to the east of somewhere and to the west of somewhere else at the same time?
- What is your method of remembering the compass points?

⑥ Shape and space skills

In this sports quiz game the teams are blindfolded and have to guess who the sportsman is just by touch. They get clues from the shapes, edges and corners that they can feel.

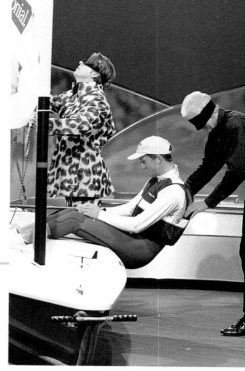

Using a set square and an A4 piece of card, construct the following squares and rectangles.

1 4 cm × 4 cm   **3** 6 cm × 3 cm
2 2 cm × 2 cm   **4** 4 cm × 2 cm

Cut these out to use as templates for exercise B.
5 How many faces are there on any cube?
6 How many faces are there on any cuboid?

Using your templates from exercise A, draw the following cubes and cuboids. The first two are done for you.

1

4 cm
4 cm
4 cm

This is a 4 x 4 x 4 cube.

2

3 cm
3 cm
6 cm

This is a 6 x 3 x 3 cuboid.

3 L = 2 cm × W = 2 cm × H = 2 cm cube
4 L = 4 cm × W = 2 cm × H = 2 cm cuboid

Describe the six different types of shapes, mentioning the number of faces, corners, edges and whether the shapes are made up from straight lines, or curved lines.

Have you ever been to an ice hockey match?

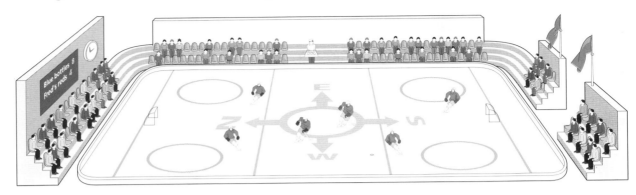

1 If the barrier around the ice rink is 50 m by 25 m, how far will the sales person have to walk to go right around the entire rink?

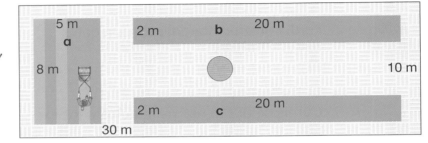

2 A gardener has to trim the borders around the outside edge of this garden. How far does he have to walk?

3 Find the perimeter of plots **a**, **b** and **c**.

4 If the gardener wanted to buy some bedding plants to go round the edge of the three rectangular plots, how many metres would he need plants for?

5 Use your calculator to work out how many plants he needs, if he plants five plants to every metre.

1 Plan a garden of your own, using a set square to make sure the corners are square. Use 1 cm to represent 1 m.

2 Write the measurements on your garden, and then calculate the perimeters.

3 How many plants would you need?

Look at the ice hockey match at the beginning of Exercise D.

1 In which direction is the blue team playing?

2 In which direction is the red team playing?

3 In which direction is the scoreboard?

4 Give the compass direction for where the flags are flying.

Now look back on your work in this lesson.
- How do you find the perimeter of a rectangle?
- How many regular 3D shapes can you name?

Module Ⓓ1–Ⓓ4

Review your skills

Number and measurement

16.07	03.Feb	29.04	13 August	07.07
09 Dec	16 March	22.08	24.11	

1 Hala works part-time in a newsagent's. Here are the dates of some magazines which people want. Put them in order by months and dates.

Pupil	Time
Yousif	101 seconds
Sarah	1 minute 15 seconds
Rheem	71 seconds
Jenny	87 secondsa
Susan	1 minute 28 seconds
John	79 seconds

2 Here are the times it takes four pupils to complete a chemistry task in the science lab. Put them in order with the fastest first.

Handling data

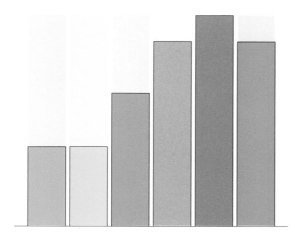

1 The average temperatures at a holiday resort are: March 23°C, April 23°C, May 25°C, June 27°C, July 28°C and August 27°C. If you plotted these on a graph, which month would have the highest point on the graph?

2 Would you expect this graph to rise or fall for the months after August?

3 On a bar chart which compares the number of people in different classes in the sports centre, two bars are exactly the same height. What does that tell you?

4 The beginner swimming class has 24 people, and the advanced swimming class has 12. What does that tell you about these two classes?

5 True or false? If I tossed a coin, I am more likely to get a 'head'.

Number and algebra

Write the heights of these students to the nearest centimetre.

1 176.7 cm   **2** 1 m 58.2 cm   **3** 145.6 cm   **4** 166.3 cm   **5** 159.9 cm

Shape and space

Use a set square and an A4 piece of card to construct the following squares and rectangles.

1 4 cm × 3 cm

2 5 cm × 7 cm

3 Draw a right-angled triangle with sides that measure 6 cm and 2 cm. Measure the third side.

4 How many faces are there on any cube?

5 How many corners are there on any cuboid?

Now try this...

Working with a partner, ask your teacher for some templates of different sized squares, rectangles, triangles and circles. Investigate the types of solid shapes you can build up using these shapes. You may need to cut some more out of card.

Find out whether it is possible or impossible to make a:

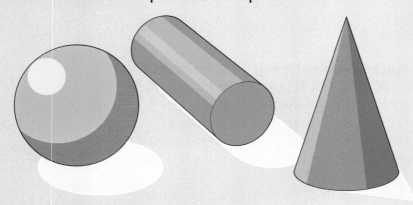

List or draw the shapes you have. Which 3D shapes can you make with them? Which ones can you not make? Why?

Check your skills

You can check how well you can do the things listed here. Get your parents and friends to help.

Number and time

1. I know the different ways of writing dates in figures, abbreviations and words.
2. I can use a calendar or a diary to make appointments and calculate time intervals.
3. I know different ways of reading clocks with hour and minute hands to the nearest minute.
4. I can estimate the time taken by daily activities in seconds or in minutes.
5. I can convert 24 hour clock time to 12 hour clock time and vice versa.

Handling data

1. I can plot points on a co-ordinate grid and join them to form a continuous graph.
2. I can read values of points in a graph in whole numbers.
3. I can read a graph which shows a general trend of increasing or decreasing.
4. I can draw a bar chart using data in clear groups.
5. I understand the idea of *evens* and can say when events are more or less likely than this.

Number and algebra

1. I can find how many sets of 10s and 100s there are in a three-digit number and can multiply and divide by 10 and 100 in practical situations.
2. When measuring, I know how to round up to a whole.
3. I know how to read to the tenth and to write this with a decimal point.
4. I know how to read counters which use zeros at the front of whole numbers.

Shape and space

1. I can name 3D shapes and do 3D drawings.
2. I can recognise 3D shapes in everyday life, and know how 3D models are made.
3. I can draw rectangles and squares using measurements of the length of sides.
4. I can measure and calculate the perimeter of shapes.
5. I understand the directions *north, east, south* and *west* on maps and can give instructions using them.

Number and algebra

① **So many of this, so many of that**
Solving mental multiplication and division problems

② **Increases, decreases and differences**
Finding the increase or decrease in a number by using the addition and subtractions on a calculator

③ **Comparing floor space**
Deciding which of several areas is bigger

④ **Relation grids**
Completing a grid from a starting entry where the rules for rows and columns are given

⑤ **Same slot, different numbers**
Using a letter or other symbol to hold or represent several different numbers

⑥ **Number and algebra skills**
Practising the skills covered in this module

Key words and phrases

number carrier
number holder
slots
symbols to represent 'any number'
symbols to stand ins for a number

decrease
difference
division as repeat subtraction
floor space
increase
maximum
multiplication as repeat addition
reduced
skip counting forwards and backwards

① So many of this, so many of that

Planning video recordings during holidays often causes family arguments. This family are only going away for a week and they can only fit five programmes on the tape. What could they do if they were going away for two weeks?

Video tapes come in small packs of two, bumper packs of five or economy packs of 20. How many tapes will Fiona have for the youth club if she buys:

1 four small packs   **3** five economy packs

2 three bumper packs   **4** four economy packs

When she gets home Fiona counts the tapes she has bought. Altogether she has 20 tapes.

5 Which pack or packs could she have bought to get 20 in total?

Solve the following problems.

1 How many chocolate bars does Andy have if he buys three packs, each containing four bars?

2 Gina collects football cards. She buys two packs of five cards. How many cards is that?

3 Bill is taping songs from the radio. So far he has taped five tracks at three minutes each. How many minutes in total has he taped?

4 At the cosmetic counter Ella chooses two different sets of three eyeshadows. How many colours is that?

5 Rachel needs batteries for her Walkman. She buys four packs of two batteries. How many does this give her?

Now solve these.

1. Karly and her two friends have won £9 on the school raffle. How much will each of them get if it is shared fairly?

2. There are 15 chocolates on the top tray of a box. How many can Alex, Duncan and Penny have each if they eat the whole tray?

3. At the school fair £2 buys 16 balls for Beat the Goalie. How many shots can each of four friends have for £2?

4. Kapil buys three multi-packs of cola. This gives her 12 cans. How many were in each pack?

5. Jane buys five family bags of crisps. She has 25 small bags in total. How many small bags were in each family bag?

On level 1 on the computer game 'Dreadzone' the player must choose one target monster to hit, and then scores the following for each direct hit.

 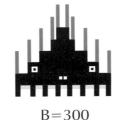  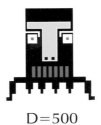

A=200   B=300   C=400   D=500

What has each of these players scored on level 1? Complete this table.

Name	Hit	Score
1 Jack		❀
2 Robby		❀
3 Emma		❀
4 Louise		❀
5 Sean		❀

Here are some level 1 scores and the targets chosen. How many of each have been hit? Complete this table.

Target monster	Score	How many?
1	1000	⚙
2	1200	⚙
3	400	⚙
4	2000	⚙
5	900	⚙

Gareth gets on to level 2 where more than one target monster can be chosen. What is his total score on each of these attempts?

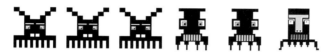

1 First try

2 Second try

3 Third try

4 Fourth try
5 If he scores more than 6000 he gets to the next level. How close does he get?

Now look back on your work in this lesson.
- Describe your method of using multiplication in your head to find solutions to problems?
- In what way are multiplication and division linked when you solve problems?

67

② Increases, decreases and differences

Most people think a car decreases in value as it gets older. Is this always true?

A

Can you solve these problems?

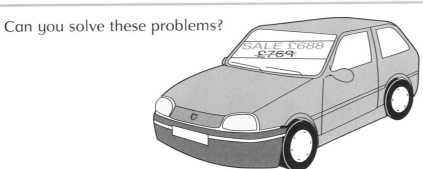

SALE £688
~~£769~~

1 By how much has this car been reduced?

2 After looking at the car, someone offers £595. What is the difference between this and the reduced price?

3 The owner of the car refuses to sell so cheaply. He says the most he will knock off the reduced price is £58. What is the cheapest price he will sell the car for?

B

By how much has each computer been reduced?

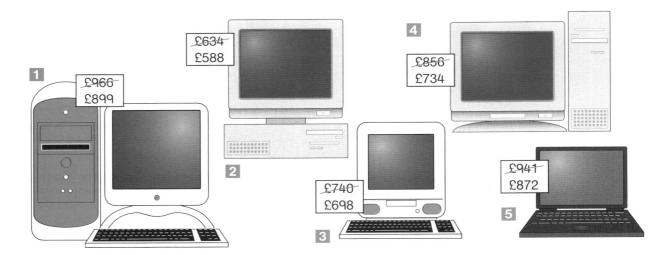

1
~~£966~~
£899

2
~~£634~~
£588

3
~~£740~~
£698

4
~~£856~~
£734

5
~~£941~~
£872

Jackie works in an electrical store on Saturdays. She is told to prepare the sale prices. Here is her list of price cuts. What is the sale price of each item?

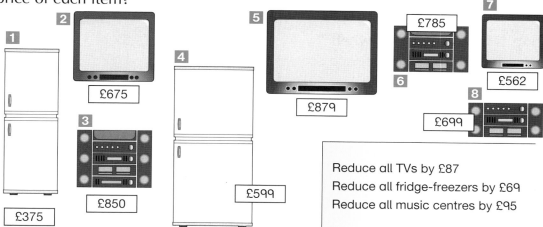

1 £375

2 £675

3 £850

4 £599

5 £879

6 £699

7 £562

8 £785

Reduce all TVs by £87
Reduce all fridge-freezers by £69
Reduce all music centres by £95

Eddie has saved money to buy a car on his 17th birthday. His parents help him to find a bargain. They look through the newspaper and make a list of the cars they are interested in and what price they will offer the owners.

	Car	Price in paper	Price they will offer
a	Ford Fiesta – C reg	£999	£870
b	Land Rover – Y reg	£875	£790
c	Vauxhall Nova – B reg	£680	£500
d	Datsun Cherry – X reg	£745	£660
e	Ford Escort – D reg	£1000	£890

1 How much money are they trying to knock off the price of each car?

The owners of the cars in the newspaper know they will not get the full price but they have a maximum amount by which they will reduce the price.

	Car	Price in paper	Maximum money off
a	Ford Fiesta – C reg	£999	£100
b	Land Rover – Y reg	£875	£90
c	Vauxhall Nova – B reg	£680	£70
d	Datsun Cherry – X reg	£745	£100
e	Ford Escort – D reg	£1000	£75

1 Which cars can Eddie buy?

Now look back on your work in this lesson.
- How do you calculate how much a price increases or decreases?
- How can the word *difference* can be used for both an increase or a decrease in a number?

③ Comparing floor space

Dancing is more enjoyable when everyone has enough *floor space* so they can move around easily.
What does floor space mean, and how is it measured?

A music agency is planning a large dance event in a town. They want the largest floor area for dancing. There are three disused warehouses where the dance could be held. They asked Shaz and Dave to find out which one is largest.

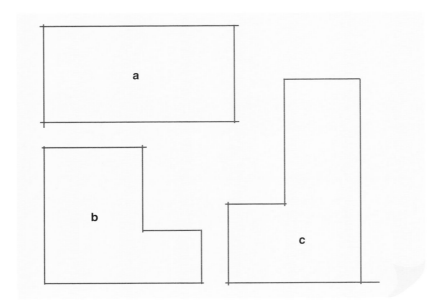

1. Shaz visited the three sites but had no measuring tape. He used a large piece of plastic sheeting. How could that be useful in measuring the floor space?

2. Dave made paper plans of the warehouses, which are to the same scale. He uses a piece of tracing paper marked with a grid to work out the area of each floor. How could this be useful? Estimate each area using this idea. Which warehouse do you think has the largest floor space?

3. What is similar and what is different about Shaz and Dave's two methods of measurement?

Lucy and her mum visit a patio centre. Here are the plans of four garden patios.

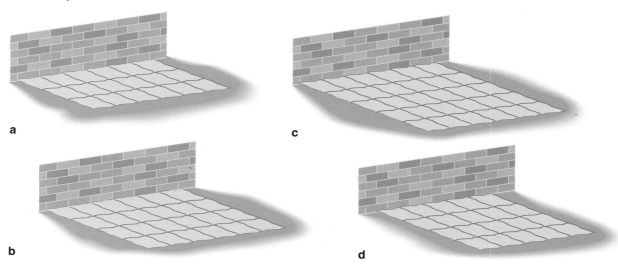

a

c

b

d

1 Lucy counts the paving stones to help her mum choose the biggest patio. Which one would Lucy choose?

2 Lucy's mum takes a few plant pots and starts counting how many pots would cover each patio. Whose method is quicker?

Helen has a lot of small presents to wrap for a Lucky Dip at the school fair. She needs to buy some wrapping paper.

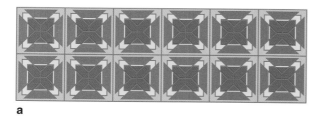

a

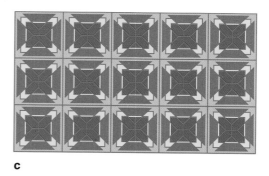

c

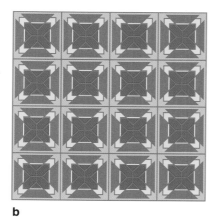

b

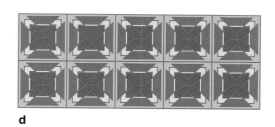

d

1 She wants to buy the largest size sheet. Which one should she buy?

Shaun and Gavin can choose one of these pitches for their stall at the school fair. They want the largest possible. Shaun looks at the following plan and uses the grids to compare areas.

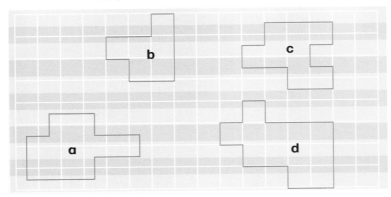

1 Which pitch should they choose?

Now solve these problems.

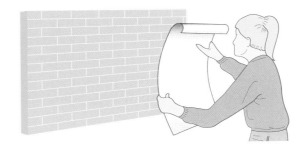

1 Wendy wants to choose the largest wall for her posters. How could she find which is larger if she has no measuring tape?

 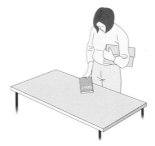

2 Sheila wants to choose the largest desk to use to do her homework. Which object should she use to help her compare areas – her folder or her diary?

Now look back on your work in this lesson.
- What is your preferred method of estimating a floor space area?
- Do you think other methods would be more useful in different situations?

4 Relation grids

Dancers are often trained to imagine the stage as a 3 by 3 grid so that they always know whether they are in the left, middle or right column to the audience, and in the front, middle or back row on the stage. In mathematics such grids are used systematically – omething happens with each step across and each step down and up.

Complete these grids.

1
add a leaf to stem | remove a petal →

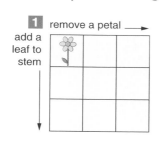

2
take 2 | add 6 →

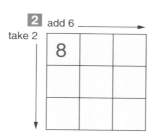

3
a What is the along rule?
b What is the down rule?

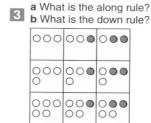

4
a What is the along rule?
b What is the down rule?

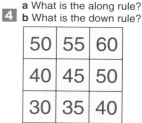

Now complete these grids.

1
add a white dot | add a black dot →

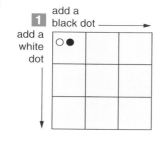

2
add a square | add a circle →

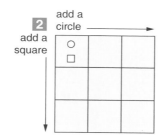

3
rotate flag a quarter turn clockwise | add a flag →

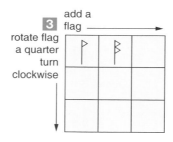

4
remove an arm | add a dot →

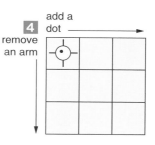

Now look at these grids. What is the along rule? What is the down rule?

1

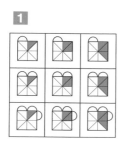

2

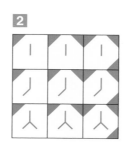

3

O×	O|O ×	O|O|O ×
O × ××	O|O ×|×	O|O|O ×|×
O ×|×|×	O|O ×|×|×	O|O|O ×|×|×

4

a	a b	a b c
A	A	A
a	a b	a b c
A B	A B	A B
a	a b	a b c
A B C	A B C	A B C

D

Complete these grids.

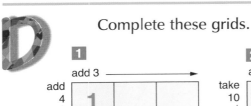

1. add 3 → / add 4 ↓ — grid with **1**

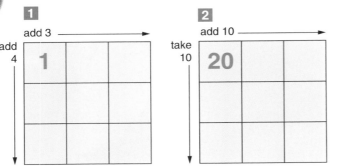

2. add 10 → / take 10 ↓ — grid with **20**

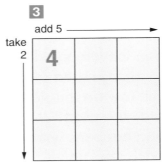

3. add 5 → / take 2 ↓ — grid with **4**

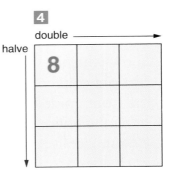

4. double → / halve ↓ — grid with **8**

E

Complete these grids. What is the down rule? What is the along rule?

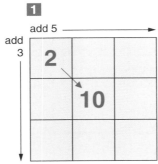

1.
5	6	7
7	8	9
9	10	11

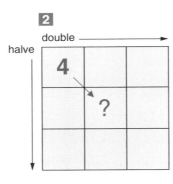

2.
1	2	4
3	6	12
9	18	36

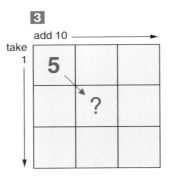

3.
10	8	6
11	9	7
12	10	8

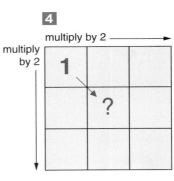

4.
2	20	200
20	200	2000
200	2000	20000

F

Complete these grids. Find the diagonal rule.

1. add 5 → / add 3 ↓ — grid with **2** and **10**

2. double → / halve ↓ — grid with **4** and **?**

3. add 10 → / take 1 ↓ — grid with **5** and **?**

4. multiply by 2 → / multiply by 2 ↓ — grid with **1** and **?**

Now look back on your work in this lesson.
- Is it easier to fill in a relation grid across or down?
- What does it mean to say that 'there are many ways of checking' in a relation grid?

⑤ Same slot, different numbers

Suppose a pigeon keeper started with ten pigeons. He then bought three more, then lost five in a storm, then won seven new ones, then two eggs hatched, then sold eight then bought 12 new. How can the pigeon keeper keep track of how many pigeons he has?

1 Adam helps his mum to run the local newsagent's. His mum gives him a pay rise of £5 for helping in the shop. You can think of his wage increase like this.

☐ —+5→ ☐

What do you think Adam may have been earning per evening and all day Saturday before his pay rise? What will his new wage be?

2 I think of a number and write it on the back of a card. I put the number in a sum. What was my number?

◯ + 2 = 5

3 Fill in the numbers to make this a correct sum.

⬡ + 7 = ☐

All the people who deliver newspapers and work part-time in the shop get a pay rise of £3. Adam makes this list of all the workers.

	Name	Old pay	New pay
a	Sarah	☐ —+3→	☐
b	John	☐ —+3→	☐
c	Tanya	☐ —+3→	☐
d	Ricky	☐ —+3→	☐
e	JT	☐ —+3→	☐
f	Anne	☐ —+3→	☐

1 Copy this list and put in the figures if Sarah and Tanya work two evenings and at present earn £14, and the others deliver papers and earn £12.

C

At Christmas Adam reduces some of the prices. He puts a notice on the wall.

ALL BOXES OF CHOCOLATE £2 OFF MARKED PRICE!
WRAPPING PAPER 30P OFF MARKED PRICE!
SELECTION BOXES £1 OFF MARKED PRICE!

He uses a reminder like this at the checkout.

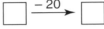

Chocolates		**Wrapping paper**		**Selection box**	
Old price	New price	Old price	New price	Old price	New price
☐ — 2 → ☐		☐ — 20 → ☐		☐ — 1 → ☐	

1 Use Adam's reminder to work out the new price for these items, which are still marked with their old prices.

> A symbol or box can be used as a number holder, or a number carrier. It makes a kind of container for numbers.

D

Ricky delivers some papers and some magazines. He delivers nine things altogether. If ❤ stands for the number of papers he delivers and ◆ stands for the number of magazines he delivers we can write:

❤ + ◆ = 9

1 Write down all the different values which ❤ and ◆ could have.
One is written for you.
4 + 5 = 9

Sarah and Tanya play a number game when the shop is quiet.
Sarah writes a symbol on three cards:

| Æ | # | ¤ |

She gives Tanya a rule.

Æ + # = ¤

Tanya must think of a set of numbers which would fit the rule.
She says:

| 4 | + | 2 | = | 6 |

Æ is 4   # is 2   ¤ is 6

4 + 2 = 6

She wins 10 points.
If she can't think of a set, Sarah turns the cards over to show her
numbers. If they make a sum which is correct, she wins 20 points.

Play this game with a partner. Remember, you can use +, − , × and ÷.
The first to 100 points wins!

Write down a set of numbers for each rule.
1 s + t = g   4 ▲ × ○ =
2 d + j = c   5 ♥ × ◆ = ☆
3 a − f = n   6 w ÷ p = t

Now look back on your work in this lesson.
• What are some advantages in having a symbol that can carry
   different numbers at different times?
• If you know that ◆ + 2 add up to more than 10, what can you
   place in the symbol ◆?

⑥ Number and algebra skills

On the hour these church bells sound twelve fast notes and then sound slow single notes for the exact time in hours. How many notes altogether will be made at 10 a.m.?
How many at 3 p.m.?

Now try to work out these problems.

1 How many chunks of chocolate would there be in four of these bars?

2 How many chocolate oranges would there be in five of these boxes?

3 How many chocolate eggs would there be in three of these boxes?

4 How many pieces of Toblerone would there be in two of these bars?

5 How many chocolate Christmas puddings would there be in three of these packs?

The local furniture is having a sale. By how much has each bedroom set been reduced?

Katie and Laura are buying a rug for the school common room.

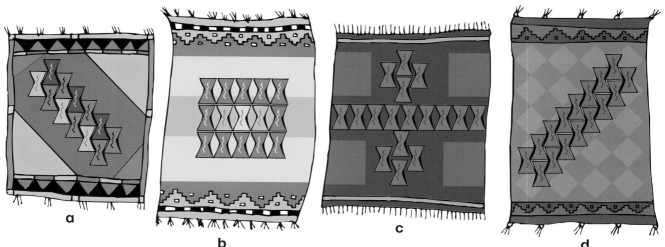

a

b

c

d

1 Which rug would cover the most floor area?

Complete these grids.

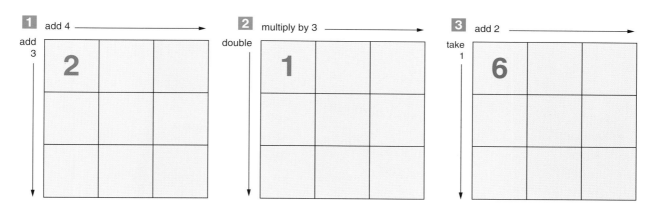

1 add 4 ⟶

add 3 ↓

2		

2 multiply by 3 ⟶

double ↓

1		

3 add 2 ⟶

take 1 ↓

6		

Find the numbers which will make these sums work.

1 ♣ + 7 = 11

2 ♣ − 3 = 12

3 ♣ + 1 = 9

4 ♣ + 6 = 16

5 ♣ − 2 = 10

6 ♣ + 5 = 35

Now look back on your work in this lesson.
- How can you use multiplication to solve real-life problems?
- Can you deal with symbols that stand in for different numbers?

Handling data

❶ How useful are surveys?
Understanding the use of surveys in everyday life

❷ Tally marks and totals
Using a tally chart to record data in groups, where each group
covers a range of numbers

❸ *And* in a database
Getting data from a database using the word *and*

❹ Overlap of sets
Using two sets of data where some elements are common to both sets

❺ Step ordering
Using and understanding a two-step ordering system

❻ Data skills
Practising skills used in surveys, data bases, overlaps in sets
and two-step ordering

Key words and phrases

frequency
graph
survey
tally chart
total in tally chart

common elements
data
database *and*
database

overlap of sets
set diagram
set intersection
two-step order

① How useful are surveys?

This is Peter Snow, the newscaster, with the *swingometer* he uses during elections. He uses it to predict the total election result after only a few results have been announced. Not all the predictions prove correct, but sometimes a few results are enough to say which party is likely to win or lose.

Rushna's class is electing a pupil to represent their class on the school council. There is a choice of six candidates and each candidate has a number. Each pupil is given a voting card like this one:

Number	Candidate	Your vote
1	John	
2	Rushna	
3	Sandra	
4	Hanif	
5	Ann	
6	Winston	

Election results

2	1	3	2	4	6
4	2	2	6	3	1
2	3	5	4	3	2
3	5	3	5	6	4
6	2	3	1	2	6
2					

Number	Candidate	Votes	Frequency
1	John	|||	3
2	Rushna	✳	✳
3	Sandra	✳	✳
4	Hanif	✳	✳
5	Ann	✳	✳
6	Winston	✳	✳

1 Here are the results of the election. Complete the tally chart for the election.

2 Who won?

George wanted to know which cake was the most popular in the country. Because he couldn't ask every single person, he decided to make a survey of his class to give him a general idea of the most popular cake in the country. Each member of his class had one vote for one of these cakes.

Cake	Votes
Cheesecake	7
Jam sponge	3
Swiss roll	4
Chocolate	10
Fruitcake	6
Battenburg	3

1 Look carefully at George's data and then construct a bar chart to show the most popular cakes.

Liz thinks that sales of the school magazine are showing a regular increase. She decides to find out by keeping a record of sales each week for six weeks.

Week	Magazine sales
Week 1	20
Week 2	25
Week 3	25
Week 4	30
Week 5	35
Week 6	40

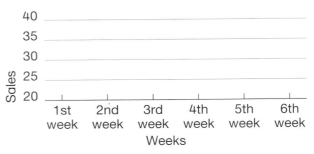

1 Look at her data. Copy the graph and then plot the points and join them together.

2 Was Liz right in thinking that there is a general trend of increasing sales of the magazine?

Answer the following questions.

1 Imagine that you wanted to get a *rough* idea of the most popular drink in the country. How would you go about finding out?

2 Name two surveys that take place in our everyday lives.

3 If you wanted to find out the most popular brand of cola in this country, would you need to ask every member of the population? Give reasons to support your answer.

4 For a school project, you need to find out approximately how many cars go past the school entrance in a day. What would you do to find out?

5 Give an example of a survey in which a tally chart would be useful.

6 Why do you think that companies sometimes carry out a survey of the popularity of their products?

Now look back on your work in this lesson.
- How useful are small surveys in predicting general patterns?
- Give an example of a time when a survey could be useful.

❷ Tally marks and totals

This is a major sorting office for post in London. Massive amounts of mail are handled there every day. First class mail is usually delivered in the UK within 24 hours of being posted.

Rushna wonders how many pieces of post are most often delivered to her house in a single day. She keeps a record for a month.

Pieces of post per day					
1	3	0	1	2	4
1	1	2	0	1	0
3	2	1	1	0	0
2	4	2	1	1	0
3	2	1	1	1	2

Pieces of post	Tally	How often
0	ЖЖ I	6
1	★	★
2	★	★
3	★	★
4	★	★

1 Copy and complete the tally chart for the amount of post that Rushna's family receives each day.

2 How many pieces of post does the family receive on most days?

Jason and Paul have an argument over how often you get a 6 when a dice is rolled. So they roll a dice 36 times and keep a record of their results.

Numbers thrown					
5	4	3	2	1	4
6	3	1	4	5	6
2	2	4	5	2	1
3	6	4	5	6	2
4	6	4	2	1	3
2	4	3	1	1	6

Number thrown	Tally	How often
1	ЖЖ I	6
2	☆	☆
3	☆	☆
4	☆	☆
5	☆	☆
6	☆	☆

1 Copy and complete the tally chart for the numbers they throw.

2 Was 6 thrown most often? If not, which number was thrown most often?

3 Why do most people use the fifth tally mark to coss over the four marks before it, making a bundle of five?

Janet wanted to find out how many days it usually rained in a week, so she kept a record for 30 weeks.

Rainy days/week

2	1	0	1	0	3
5	3	2	1	1	0
2	1	5	3	4	2
4	6	5	6	3	2
1	0	1	0	2	2

Rainy days in a week	Tally	Frequency
0	ⲎⳀ	5
1	✷	✷
2	✷	✷
3	✷	✷
4	✷	✷
5	✷	✷
6	✷	✷

1 Copy and complete the tally chart for the number of days that it rained each week.

Look carefully at these words below.

Alan	train	book	banana	Jaffa
rabbit	television	canal	computer	hearsay
England	Arabia	France	Australia	Italy
sultana	present	avail	eleven	remark
Havana	alarm	attain	file	retain

Number of 'a's	Tally	Frequency
0	⟲	⟲
1	⟲	⟲
2	⟲	⟲
3	⟲	⟲

1 How many times does the letter **a** appear in each word? Complete the tally chart.

Now look back on your work in this lesson.
- What is the difference between the 'Tally' column and the 'Frequency' (how often) column in a tally chart?
- Why does crossing through each group of five tally marks help you to count the numbers?

③ *And* in a database

A record company is forming a new boy band and wants a boy with hair that is dark and curly to complete the line up. Whom should they reject?

Sarah works in her local supermarket on Saturdays. She checks the stock on the computer. Here are some of the lists of items that she uses. She knows that the same item may be on more than one list.

Frozen
peas
broad beans
mixed vegetables
cauliflower
fish fingers
beefburgers
cod-in-sauce
cheesecake
Black Forest gateaux
profiteroles
ice cream

Fresh
tomatoes
doughnuts from bakery
scones from bakery
onions
carrots
cheesecake

Sweet
cheesecake
Black Forest gateaux
profiteroles
doughnuts
scones
ice cream

Savoury
peas
broad beans
mixed vegetables
cauliflower
fish fingers
beefburgers
cod-in-sauce
tomatoes

Think of these lists as a database. Use your database to answer these questions.

1 Which of the items are both frozen and savoury?
2 Which of the items are frozen and sweet?
3 Which of the items are fresh and sweet?
4 Which of the items are fresh and savoury?
5 Is cheesecake available in both fresh and frozen forms?
6 Are beefburgers available both fresh and frozen?

Think about even numbers. Now think about the numbers that are in the 3× table.

1 Write in your book 10 different even numbers.

2 Write in your book 10 different numbers that are in the 3× table.

3 Look at your answers to question 1 and question 2. Write down all the numbers that are in both of your answers.

4 Is 12 both even and in the 3× table?

5 Is 27 both even and in the 3× table?

6 Is 16 both even and in the 3× table?

Hannah works in the electrical department of a big store. She keeps a database of the stock in the department. Here are her lists.

Enter the above lists into a database. Then look at your database and write the answers to the following questions in your book.

1 Which items cost more than £100 and are used outdoors?

2 Which items cost less than £100 and are used outdoors?

3 Which items cost more than £100 and are used indoors?

4 Which items cost less than £100 and are used indoors?

5 Is the hairdryer used indoors or outdoors? Does it cost more or less than £100?

6 Is the lamp used indoors or outdoors? Does it cost more or less than £100?

Paul decides to make up his own list of car registrations and to enter them on a database.

He gives all cars a letter to show when they were made.

1998 – S	1996 – Q	1994 – N
1997 – R	1995 – P	1993 – M

This letter is the first symbol on the registration.

He gives each colour a number.

Blue – 1	White – 3	Green – 5
Red – 2	Black – 4	Orange – 6

This is the first number of the registration.

Here are the registration numbers that Paul made up.

Look at Paul's data and then answer these questions.

1. What is the registration number of the white car made in 1998?
2. What are the colours of the two cars made in 1997?
3. Write down the registration numbers of the blue cars made in 1993.
4. What are the colours of the cars made in 1994?
5. In which years were the black cars made?
6. In which year was the orange car made?

Rosanne is interested in the football strips of different clubs. She keeps a record of all the teams that have red as their main colour and all the teams that have blue as their main colour.

👕 Red teams

Barnsley	Southampton
Bournemouth	Liverpool
Charlton Athletic	Leyton Orient
Manchester United	Brentford
Middlesborough	Stoke City
Sheffield United	Wrexham

👕 Blue teams

Blackburn Rovers	Oldham Athletic
Brighton & Hove Albion	Portsmouth
Carlisle United	Queens Park Rangers
Gillingham	Sheffield Wednesday
Chelsea	Manchester City
Everton	Huddersfield Town

She makes up two more lists from her listed clubs to show clubs that are from the North and clubs that are from the South.

Teams from the North

Barnsley	Liverpool
Blackburn Rovers	Oldham Athletic
Manchester United	Sheffield Wednesday
Middlesborough	Manchester City
Sheffield United	Huddersfield Town
Carlisle United	Stoke City
Everton	Wrexham

Teams from the South

Bournemouth	Chelsea
Charlton Athletic	Portsmouth
Brighton & Hove Albion	Queens Park Rangers
Gillingham	Brentford
Southampton	Leyton Orient

Rushna enters her lists in a database. What should her answers be to these questions?

1 Which northern clubs play in red?
2 Which southern clubs play in blue?
3 Which northern clubs play in blue?
4 Which southern clubs play in red?
5 Name the colour that Leyton Orient play in. Are they a northern or a southern club?
6 Name the colour that Huddersfield Town play in. Are they from the North or from the South?

Now look back on your work in this lesson.
- What is a database?
- What is the possible confusion in using the word *and* in a database and in daily speech?

④ Overlap of sets

This is Dennis Rodman of the Chicago Bulls. His coloured hair makes him noticeable on the basketball court. What do you think about this hairstyle?

Trevor carries out a survey of hairstyles in his class. Here are his findings.

a Trevor, Simon, Hussain, Becky, Vicky, Joanne and Curtley all have black hair. The rest of the class do not have black hair.

b Anna, Shripa, Maureen, Trevor, Hussain and Becky all have straight hair. The rest of the class do not have straight hair.

c Francesca, Paul, Ben, Gussav, Trevor, Joanne, Shripa and Anna all have long hair. The rest of the class have short hair.

Think about this information and then answer these questions.
1 Draw a set diagram showing who has straight, black hair.
2 Draw a set diagram showing who has long, black hair.
3 What do you know about Becky's hair?
4 Describe Trevor's hair.
5 Name everyone who has straight, black hair.
6 Name everyone who has long, black hair.

Winston and his friends go to their favourite burger bar. This is what they have to eat.

a Winston, George, Jenny, Anjum, Bill and Hanif have beefburgers.

b Winston, Jenny, Bill, Hanif, Rita, John and James have French fries.

c Wayne, Sammy, Debbie, Andrea, Val, Winston, George and Bill have chicken nuggets.

Think about this information and then answer these questions.
1 Draw a set diagram showing who has beefburgers and French fries.
2 Draw a set diagram showing who has chicken nuggets and French fries.
3 What does George have to eat?
4 Name everyone who has beefburger, chicken nuggets and French fries.
5 What does Jenny have to eat?
6 Name everyone who has French fries only.

C

Simon belongs to a music club. It helps pupils to practise playing three instruments – piano, guitar and drums.

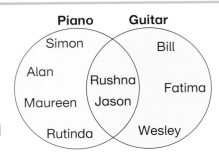

Jason, Bill, Wesley, Pete and Val play the drums.

Think about this information and then answer these questions.

1 How many pupils play both the piano and the guitar?

2 Draw a set diagram of those pupils who play the piano and drums. Do not show the guitar set.

3 Who plays the piano, the guitar and the drums?

4 Which instruments does Bill play?

5 Which instruments does Simon play?

6 Which instruments does Rushna play?

D

Debbie carried out a survey to find out the favourite television programmes of members of her class. The three most popular programmes were Eastenders, Match of the Day and Countdown. She made a list of who watched each of these programmes.

a Debbie, George, Hanif, Rachid, Joanne, Vicky and Dave all watched EastEnders. The rest of the class did not watch EastEnders.

b Debbie, George, Sam, Sue, Teresa and Jackie all watched Match of the Day. The rest of the class did not watch Match of the Day.

c Dave, Debbie, Sam, Teresa, Harry, Joanne and Abdul all watched Countdown. The rest of the class did not watch Countdown.

Think about this information and then answer these questions.

1 Draw a set diagram of the pupils that watched EastEnders and Match of the Day.

2 Draw a set diagram of the pupils that watched EastEnders and Countdown.

3 Which programmes does Sam watch?

4 Who watches all three programmes?

5 Which programmes does Teresa watch?

6 Which programmes does Dave watch?

Now look back on your work in this lesson.
- What can a set diagram show that a bar chart can not?
- How many subsets can you find if you have two intersecting sets?

⑤ Step ordering

Wembley Stadium holds nearly 100 000 people. It is a massive job to get all the spectators seated in their correct seats. This is done by splitting the seating areas into Blocks, such as Block F. The Blocks are then divided into Entrances, such as 71.

How is this helpful to the spectators who need to find their seats?

Harry helps in the ticket office of his local football club. He needs to put some tickets in order so that blocks of continuous tickets can be sold together.

These are the tickets he is given:

A53	E71	E15	C55	D29
B24	C58	C54	E16	B26
C57	A51	B23	B25	D27
A55	B22	C56	E18	D31
C59	D28	A52	D30	E19

Answer these questions.

1. Put all the numbers in Row A in order.
2. Put all the numbers in Row B in order.
3. Put all the numbers in Row C in order.
4. Put all the numbers in Row D in order.
5. Put all the numbers in Row E in order.
6. How many tickets are there altogether?

The controller at the bus station needs to make sure that all the buses are at their correct stands.

These are the bus numbers. The letter indicates the stand.

1. Arrange the buses by stand and in number order.

A15	B35	C17	D33	B32	C15
E26	A17	B30	A16	D32	E27
F38	D30	F35	B34	C16	D31
E25	A13	B31	C19	D29	A14
A12	B33	C18	D28	F36	C20
E30	F37	E28	F33	E29	F34

The postman has to arrange the mail in order before he delivers it. He does this for the buildings at a nearby estate. The buildings are named after fruits.

| Peach (PE) | Plum (PL) | Strawberry (ST) |
| Sultana (SU) | Avocado (AV) | Apricot (AP) |

Look at the addresses and then answer these questions.

1 Write down all the numbers for Peach (PE).
2 Write down all the numbers for Plum (PL).
3 Write down all the numbers for Strawberry (ST).
4 Write down all the numbers for Sultana (SU).
5 Write down all the numbers for Avocado (AV).
6 Write down all the numbers for Apricot (AP).

Mail to deliver

PE29	ST53	AV84
PL28	AP83	PE30
ST54	AP84	SU52
SU55	ST50	PE26
AV80	SU57	PL29
AP86	PL31	SU56
SU53	PL32	AP82
AV82	ST51	AP85
ST52	AV83	PE28
PL30	AV81	PE27

Peter works in an office that arranges tennis courses for under-16 players. He has the forms of five players from each of these counties.

| Yorkshire (Y) | Warwickshire (W) | Sussex (S) |
| Lancashire (L) | Devon (D) | Essex (E) |

Each player has his own number. Peter needs to put the forms in order.

Write the answers to these questions.

1 Write down the numbers of the Yorkshire (Y) players.
2 Write down the numbers of the Warwickshire (W) players.
3 Write down the numbers of the Sussex (S) players.
4 Write down the numbers of the Lancashire (L) players.
5 Write down the numbers of the Devon (D) players.
6 Write down the numbers of the Essex (E) players.

Tennis players

W7	Y6	S10
S9	L11	D10
E16	D12	Y4
Y2	E14	S6
L8	D11	W4
D14	W5	S8
Y5	L9	E12
E15	S7	L12
E13	W6	D13
L10	Y3	W8

Roy works in a warehouse and today he is sorting out T-shirts. There are four sizes: small (S), medium (M), large (L) and extra large (XL). There are five different colours: black, red, white, yellow and green. There is one shirt in each colour in all of the sizes. Roy needs to put them in order.

1 List by colour the size of every shirt that Roy should have.
2 Now list by size the colours of every shirt that Roy should have.

Now look back on your work in this lesson.
• Think of the different situations where two-step ordering is needed.
• What were the best ways you found of putting the lists in order?

⑥ Data skills

Some London Underground stations are also on British Rail lines. How do you know which tube stations connect with British Rail lines?

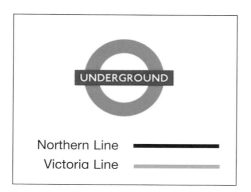

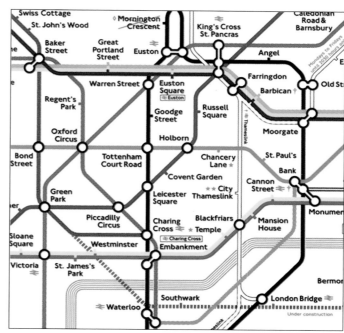

Look at the Underground map and then answer these questions.

1 Make a list of all the stations that are on the Victoria Line and the Northern Line, *and* are British Rail stations. Remember to look for the sign.

Look carefully at the Victoria, Northern Line and British Rail stations when answering these questions.

2 Which stations are on the Victoria Line and are British Rail stations?

3 Which stations are on the Northern Line and are British Rail stations?

4 Which stations are on the Victoria Line and on the Northern Line?

5 Which stations are on the Victoria Line, but not on the Northern Line, and nor are they British Rail stations?

6 Which stations are on the Northern Line but not on the Victoria Line, and nor are they British Rail stations?

Odd numbers are numbers that end in 1, 3, 5, 7, or 9.
Now think about the numbers that are in the 5× table.
Answer these questions.

1 Write down 10 odd numbers.

2 Write down 10 numbers that are in the 5× table.

3 Look at your answers to question 1 and question 2. Write down all of the numbers that are in both of your answers.

4 What do you notice about your answer to question 3?

5 Is 25 odd and in the 5× table?

6 Is 40 even and in the 5× table?

Adrian and Simon have an argument over which is the most popular colour of car. They decide to find out. They count the colours of cars that pass the school gates during a time period of 15 minutes. These are the colours that they count.

Blue (B)	Orange (O)	White (W)
Green (G)	Red (R)	

Here are their findings.

Make and complete a tally chart for the colour of cars, using these headings:

Colour of car	Tally	Frequency

Car colours

R	B	R	W	W
O	B	R	W	R
G	R	W	B	W
R	W	R	G	B
W	W	R	B	O
R	B	R	R	W

1 Which colour was the most popular?
2 Which colour was second most popular?

At Sarah's school there are five classes in each of the years 7 to 11. Here are the names of the form tutors for each year.

Year 7	Year 8	Year 9	Year 10	Year 11
Ms Palmer	Ms Watkins	Ms Patel	Mr White	Mr Watson
Mr Shah	Mr Smith	Mr Lawrenson	Ms Evans	Mr Jenkins
Mrs Jones	Mrs Hunter	Mr Black	Mr Gibbons	Ms Brown
Ms Wilson	Mr Armstrong	Mrs Fox	Ms Johnston	Ms Khan
Mr Adams	Mr Peters	Mr Hughes	Mr Desai	Mr Anderson

Each class has the year number followed by the initial of the teacher's name. For example, Miss Patel's class is 9P.

What is the class number for these pupils?

1 Sarah is in Mr Shah's class.
2 Hanif and Rachid are in Mrs Fox's class.
3 Winston is in Mr Jenkin's class.
4 Debbie is in Mr White's class.
5 Shripa is in Mr Adam's class.
6 Alison is in Ms Evans' class.

Now look back on your work in this lesson.
- How can two-step ordering be used in a survey?
- Can you think of a connection between the overlap of two sets and the use of the word *and* in using a database?

Number and measurement

❶ Inches and feet
Knowing and using sizes in inches and feet

❷ Millimetres
Knowing and using sizes in millimetres and centimetres

❸ It must fit exactly
Using a ruler or tape marked and numbered in millimetres to make measurements

❹ Ounces, pounds, stones and tons
Knowing what things are weighed in ounces, pounds, stones and tons

❺ Grams, kilograms and tonnes
Knowing what things are weighed in grams and kilograms

❻ Measurement skills
Practising the use of imperial and metric measurements

Key words and phrases
imperial measure
ounce, pound, stone, ton
foot, inch, dozen
metric measures
grams, kilograms, tonnes
millimetre, centimetre
exact
estimate
accurate, more accurate
approximately
nearest mark

① Inches and feet

In the past, measuring was done using handspans, feet or cubits. What problems can you imagine with using such measures?
It is said that the standard unit *foot* was the length of one of an early king's feet. Do you think this could be true?
We can estimate the length of small objects by knowing that:
- a joint of your little finger is about an *inch*
- a *foot* is a bit longer than your foot.

 Look carefully at a ruler that is marked in inches like this one. Is the top joint of your little finger one inch long? If not, choose a finger that is more accurate. Now put your ruler out of sight.

Inches					
0	1	2	3	4	5

Centimetres
0 1 2 3 4 5 6 7 8 9 10 11 12 13

1 Choose three items from your pencil case. Estimate and write down their length in inches, using the part of the finger you chose to help you.
2 Now measure the same items in inches with your ruler and write down the lengths.
3 Were your estimates good? If not, try this exercise again.

 Six pupils have each grown a daffodil bulb at school. They can take their bulb home when the plants have grown to 1 foot tall. Marie's daffodil bulb is 8 inches tall, Rahkee's is 7 inches tall, Tom's is 11 inches tall, Philip's is 10 inches tall, Sarah's is 12 inches tall and Ali's is 9 inches tall.

1 Will any of the pupils be able to take their bulb home today?
2 Who is the most likely to take their bulb home next?
3 How many inches does Rakhee's bulb have to grow before she can take it home?
4 Will Ali take his bulb home after it has grown 4 inches?

Compare your own foot with the foot ruler.

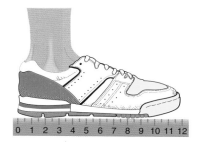

1 Find three items that are about a foot long in the classroom.
2 Measure them with your ruler.
3 Were your choices really about a foot long?
4 Choose one item that was shorter than a foot. How many inches shorter was it?
5 Choose one item that was longer than a foot. How many inches longer was it?

Now answer these questions.
1 Estimate how many feet it is from your chair to the door.
2 Measure the distance and see how accurate your answer is.

Farah's mum is knitting her a jumper. The back has to be 1 foot and 8 inches long.
On Monday she knits the first 6 inches of the back. On Tuesday she knits 5 inches more.
1 How long is the back now?
2 How much must she knit on Wednesday to finish off this part of the jumper?

Ten inch nails were used in this job. Each nail is marked with the height that still shows above the piece of wood. You can use a shorthand for inches like this:". How far has each one been hammered into the wood?

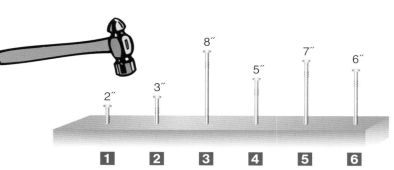

Now look back on your work in this lesson.
• What makes a good estimator? Were you a good one?
• Can you remember which bit of your finger was about an inch long?

② Millimetres

Insects and spiders come in many sizes. People are often quite happy to find a money spider walking up their arm! They are very small and are said to bring you good luck with money. It takes someone a little braver to cope with a tarantula.

How many times bigger than a money spider is a tarantula?

Here is part of a ruler that is marked in millimetres.
Remember to start measuring from 0, and to measure to the nearest mark.

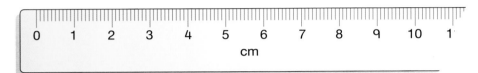

cm

1 There are some cases where it is not important that two measurements of the same thing differ by one millimetre. Can you think of any?

2 Name six items that it would be sensible to measure in millimetres because of their size.

Can you estimate accurately?

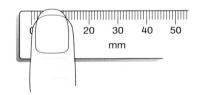

1 Estimate the width of your thumb in millimetres without measuring.

2 Now use your ruler or the ruler at the top of the page to get an accurate measurement.

Now can you estimate accurately?

1 Estimate the width of your wrist without measuring.

2 Check your estimate. How close was it to the actual measurement?

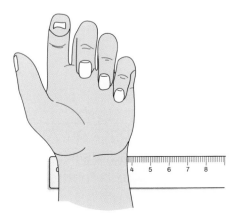

Write your whole name in your book as neatly as you can!

1 Estimate and then use a ruler marked in millimetres to measure your first name.

2 Do the same with your middle name or names, if you have any.

3 Do the same with your surname.

4 Add together the lengths of all your names.

5 Now measure how long your name is altogether.

6 This measurement should be longer than your answer to question 3. Why?

Copy this table and use it to fill in your answers.

Item	Estimate	Measure

1 Find several small items from your pencilcase or classroom.

2 Estimate their length or width in millimetres and then check your guess using the ruler.

Draw a similar table to the one in exercise E to record your results.

1 Estimate the length of five or six of your pencils, felt tips or pens.

2 Now measure them using the ruler.

3 Do you think that using millimeters for a measurement gives a clearer method of comparing the lengths than using centimeters alone?

Now look back on your work in this lesson.

- Do you think it is easier to give measurements using the metric system than the old system?
- Do you think you can choose the correct metric unit to use, simply by looking at the size of the item?

❸ It must fit exactly

Kitchen units need to be fitted as accurately as possible in order to make the best use of the space in the kitchen. Their measurements are given in millimetres because the small measures help to fill spaces more exactly.

A How good are you at measuring accurately?

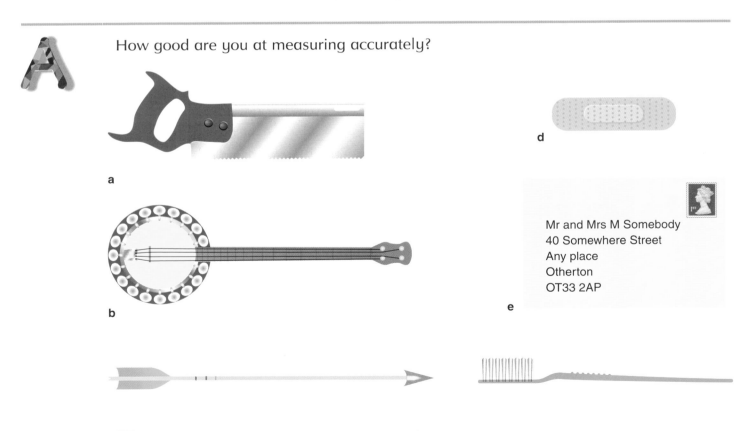

1 Use your ruler to measure the length of these pictures in millimetres.

Try measuring some lines.

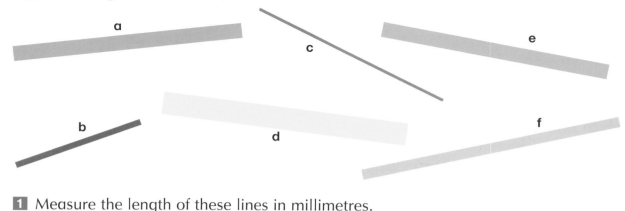

1 Measure the length of these lines in millimetres.

Draw lines of these lengths using your millimetre ruler.

1 55 mm   **4** 120 mm

2 78 mm   **5** 113 mm

3 94 mm   **6** 64 mm

A sink unit is 950 mm, a base unit with work top is 900 mm and a fridge–freezer is 540 mm. Answer these questions, using a calculator to help you.

1 What is the total length of the three items placed side by side?

2 The length of the kitchen wall is 3.5 m. Change this measurement to millimetres.

3 If the three items are fitted along the wall, how much space is left?

Extra base units come in three sizes: 1000 mm, 1100 mm and 1500 mm.

1 Choose the best cabinet to go in the space that was left in exercise D, question 3.

2 How big is the gap that is now left?

3 Will this gap matter?

If the top units are 1100 mm long, how many will fit along the wall above?

> Now look back on your work in this lesson.
> * Explain how millimetres, centimetres and metres are related to each other.
> * Explain how you can tell which nails are 10mm long and which are 25 mm long from a box of nails of different lengths.

④ Ounces, pounds, stones and tons

Heavy vehicles have to be weighed before they are allowed to go on the road. This is done on a weighbridge. The heaviest loaded lorry which is allowed on the road is 40 ton.
A ton is the weight of a large car, 10 rugby players, or 20 washing machines.
About how many pupils together may weigh about a ton?

Ounce	A slice of bread	
Pound	Four small apples	(16 oz)
Stone	A child about 1 year old	(14 lb
Ton	A van	(160 st)

A

What imperial measure would you use to find the weight of the following things?
1. Flour to go in a cake mixture
2. A sack of potatoes
3. A boxer before a match
4. Concrete to build a bridge
5. Gold to make a tiara
6. A bag of sugar

B

Which one of the following would be the correct weight of these items?

2 lb
20 lb
200 lb

1

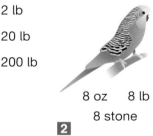

8 oz   8 lb
8 stone

2

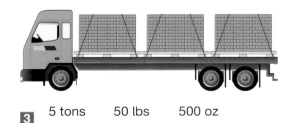

3   5 tons   50 lbs   500 oz

C

When Darren was born he weighed 9 lbs. By the time he was 14 he weighed 8 st 10 lb.
When Marian was born she weighed 6 lb. At 14 Marian weighs 8 st 8 lb.
1. Which person has gained the most weight since birth, and by how much?

Here are eight different objects. Match them to the weights given.

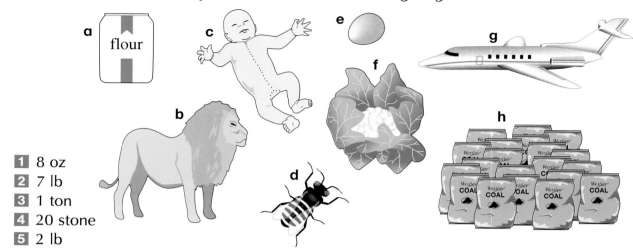

1 8 oz
2 7 lb
3 1 ton
4 20 stone
5 2 lb
6 2 oz
7 Have you got two items left over? Suggest what they weigh, using the expressions *more than* and *less than*.

There is a group of American exchange students working with Zak's Maths class today. The teacher asks them to tell her pupils their weight. Here is the list they make.

Student name	Weight
Brad	120 pounds
Sam	114 pounds
Shelly	95 pounds
Mel	135 pounds
Gina	107 pounds
Juan	98 pounds

1 Which of the students is the heaviest?
2 Which two are closest in weight?
3 Zak knows that he weighs 8 stone 2 lb. There are 14 lb in a stone. Which of the American students weighs the same as Zak?

Work out the weight of the other American students in stones and pounds, and write a new list in your book.

Now look back on your work in this lesson.
- How can you estimate a person's weight to the nearest one or two stones?
- Can you do the estimate in kilograms?

⑤ Grams, kilograms and tonnes

What unit of weight would you use to weigh the toilet paper in this picture? What would you use to weigh the puppy?

 Tins always give the weight of their contents on the label.

1 Which tin has the heaviest contents?
2 If you bought two large tins of beans what weight of beans would you get?
3 If I eat a small tin of peas and a small tin of carrots with my dinner, what weight of vegetables do I eat?
4 Which two tins contain the lightest amount of food?

 Which metric unit of weight would you use to weigh the following?
1 Sugar to go in a cake mixture
2 A sack of charcoal
3 A small child
4 A lorry on a weighbridge
5 A letter to post
6 A packet of jelly

C Here are six different weights. Choose an item to go with each weight.

a   b   c   d   e   f

1 80 g   **3** 1 tonne   **5** 6 g

2 500 g   **4** 80 kg   **6** 200 g

D Caroline and her sister are making a chocolate sponge cake.
All the ingredients need to be the same weight.
They weigh an egg and find that it weighs 70 g.

1 There are three eggs to go in the cake. About how much will they weigh to the nearest hundred grams?

2 What will be the weight of the sugar and the fat?

3 The flour and cocoa powder together should weigh the same as the eggs. They use 180 g of flour. How much cocoa is needed?

4 Give the total weight of the ingredients (three eggs, sugar, fat, flour and cocoa).

E Now answer these problems.

1 A bag of sugar weighs 1 kg. Rachel's family use about 125 g a day. Roughly how long will one bag last?

2 Brendan's family use twice as much sugar. How long will the bag last them?

3 About how many packets will Brendan's mum have to buy in February (28 days)?

F Correct the mistakes in these sentences.

1 When Sara's sister was born she weighed 4 g.

2 Last winter we burnt 1 kg of coal on our open fire.

3 The diet only allows you to eat 1 tonne of potatoes in a week.

4 Carlos gave his weight as 90 g.

5 A small bag of flour weighs 500 kg.

Now look back on your work in this lesson.
- How many grams are in a kilogram?
- Can you remember the kind of items that are weighed with grams and kilograms? Think of some things that would need weighing in tonnes.

⑥ Measurement skills

The Great Wall of China is over 4,500 miles long. If all the bricks were taken from the section of it that was built during the Ming dynasty, you could build a five-foot high wall all around the Earth.

Joseph's dad is building a 6 foot wall. On Saturday morning he measures the wall when he has laid two rows. The wall is 6 inches high.

1. By how much does the wall grow with each new row of bricks?
2. If 12 inches make 1 foot, how many rows must he build before the wall is 1 foot high?
3. He lays 16 rows on Saturday. How high is the wall?
4. How many rows are left to lay on Sunday?

You need to measure six items.
Write down the most sensible metric measure to use (mm/cm/m) for each.
Think about their size and how accurate you need to be.

1. The length of your garden
2. The glass for a window
3. The width of the front door
4. The height of a tree
5. The length of the hall
6. A screw head

Now answer these questions.

1. Estimate and write down the width of your hand span in centimetres without measuring.
2. Use a ruler to check your estimate.
3. Now estimate the length of your arm using your hand span to help you.
4. Check your estimate with a suitable measure.
5. Was your arm longer or shorter than half a metre?

D Draw lines of these lengths in your book, using your ruler.

1 5 cm
2 78 mm
3 9 cm
4 145 mm
5 113 mm
6 8.6 mm

E Answer these questions.

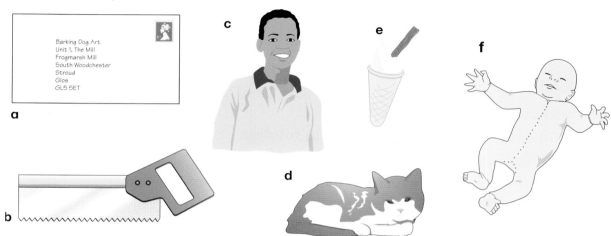

1 Put these items in order of weight starting with the lightest.

5 g	55 kg	9 kg	150 g	4 kg	600 g

2 Choose which one of these would be a sensible weight for each of the items.

F Sweets used to be sold in 4 oz and 8 oz packets.

1 Which packet was the same weight as half a pound?
2 Which one was the same as a quarter of a pound?
3 If you needed 12 oz of sweets which packets would you buy?
4 If a 4 oz packet contains 12 sweets, how many sweets would you get if you bought a packet weighing one pound?

Now look back on your work in this lesson.
- If you had the choice would you measure and weigh using the imperial or metric system?
- Give reasons for why your choice is a good one and some reasons for why it is not.

Module Ⓓ8

Shape and space

❶ Co-ordinate detectives
Identifying a position on a grid using co-ordinates

❷ Perfect fit
Matching up congruent shapes and pictures

❸ Meshed cogs
Understanding how meshed cogs turn clockwise and anti-clockwise, faster and slower

❹ Shapes sliding and turning
Recognising the ways shapes can be moved to new positions: reflection, sliding, rotating

❺ Rotation symmetry
Investigating the patterns made using rotation

❻ Shape and space skills
Practising finding positions on a co-ordinate grid, congruent shapes, meshed cogs and rotation symmetry

Key words and phrases

line of reflection
mirror line
order of rotational symmetry
point of rotation
reflection
rotation
translation

circular protractor
clockwise
anti-clockwise
congruent, perfect fit
degrees in a circle – 360°
speed of turn
direction of turn
touching cogs

co-ordinates
grid
horizontal axis
vertical axis
position
zero start

❶ Co-ordinate detectives

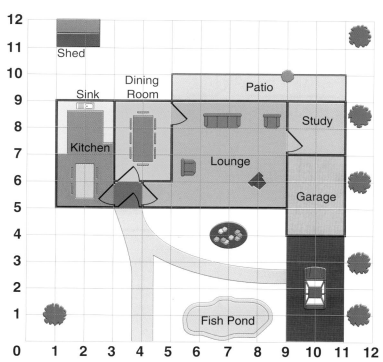

Sometimes detectives rely on detailed maps to solve crimes, which use *co-ordinates*.
If you want to become a detective then you need to practise using these skills.
What does 'The two co-ordinates give you a point, not a square' mean?

A murder has been committed at this house. The police are at the scene. Help them to find out who is responsible!
Look at the plan of the house and garden, and describe the position of the main items.
It helps the police if you can give them the co-ordinates. Remember to go along first, then up.

> **Co-ordinates** are numbers which describe the place a point occupies in a grid.

Complete these sentences. The first one is done for you.
1 The car is at co-ordinates (10,2).
2 The flower bed is at (__,__).
3 The TV is in the lounge at co-ordinates (__,__).
4 The kitchen sink is at (__,__).

Now write what you can see in these positions.
5 (1,1)
6 (2,6)
7 (2,11)
8 (10,8)

Earlier in the day the murdered man had been to the sports centre.

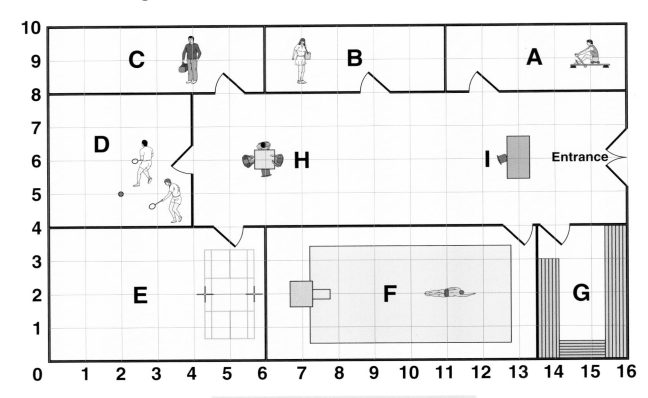

A fitness room
B female changing room
C male changing room
D squash courts
E main hall (badminton)
F swimming pool
G sauna
H main entrance
I information desk

Write down the names of the rooms the man would have entered
if he used the doors at the following co-ordinates.

1 (12,8)   **3** (13,4)   **5** (4,6)
2 (5,8)   **4** (14,4)   **6** (5,4)

Give the co-ordinates for the following.
1 The girl in the changing room
2 The position of the ball in the squash court
3 The diving board
4 The swimmer wearing a blue costume
5 The information desk at the entrance
6 The rowing machine in the fitness room

D Make a list of the different people that might have seen the man on that day. Think where he would have passed by.

E The man returned home, and was murdered. Someone had followed him. Find out who did this terrible crime. Where did it happen? Use this grid to solve it. Each line is one word.

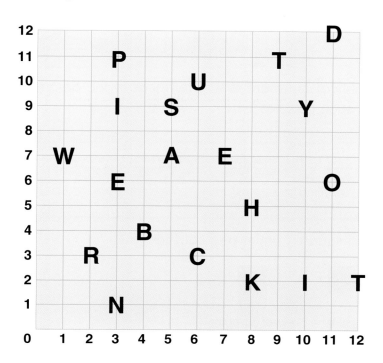

1 (2,3) (7,7) (6,3) (3,6) (3,11) (9,11) (10,2) (11,6) (3,1) (3,9) (5,9) (12,2)

2 (10,2) (3,1)

3 (9,11) (8,5) (3,6)

4 (8,2) (3,9) (12,2) (6,3) (8,5) (7,7) (3,1)

You have now solved the mystery!

F Write this message using pairs of co-ordinates from the grid in exercise E as clues.

On your birthday.

Now look back on your work in this lesson.
- Can you label and use a co-ordinate grid where the horizontal and vertical lines are not numbered?
- Can you continue a co-ordinate grid to the right and up, if you need to include other areas?

② **Perfect fit**

1   2

Spot the difference puzzles look identical but there are differences in the details.
What is the best way of making up such puzzles?

What are the six differences in the pictures above?

Copy these shapes on to squared paper and cut them out.

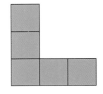

1 Place one of the shapes on squared paper. Draw round the shape.

2 Using the same shape, move it to a different position on the paper. Turn it round to face a different way. Draw round the shape in its new position.

3 Find two other places on the paper and draw round your shape again.

4 Now take another shape and repeat these instructions.

5 Do this with the third shape.

6 Make up a new shape of your own, and draw it facing in different directions.

You should now have 16 shapes on your paper.

7 Colour each shape in one colour, using a different colour for each different shape.

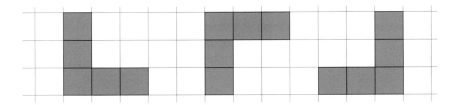

We call identical shapes *congruent shapes*.

Look at the picture of the boats.

1 Match the boats that are congruent. Write down the letters to identify the pairs.

Cut out three shapes of your own. For example:

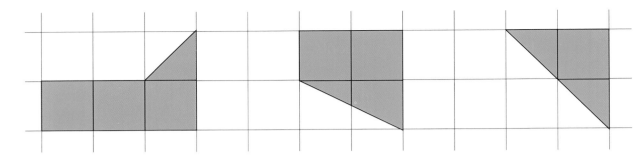

1 On a piece of squared paper, draw each of these shapes twice, facing in different directions.
2 Shade them in so that they are all the same colour. Label the shapes **a** to **f**.
3 Now give these shapes to a friend to match together.

Match these pairs of shapes.

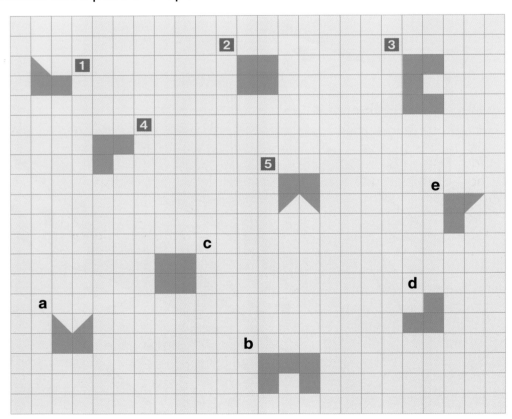

Now look back on your work in this lesson.
- What words are used to describe shapes that fit each other perfectly even if they are drawn facing different ways?
- How many different ways can a shape face on a square grid?

③ Meshed cogs

Cogs are very important in driving things – from steam engines to watches. The speed and direction things go in depends on the way the cogs mesh together.

Look at these crosses.

1 Using thick card, make two crosses of your own. Pierce a hole in the centre of each of them.
2 Fix the crosses to a piece of paper, with a paper fastener, so that the two crosses just touch each other. One cross needs to be slightly lower than the other, as shown above.
3 Turn the top cross in a clockwise direction. This will make the lower cross move. Describe the direction that the lower cross is moving.
4 What happens if you move the lower cross in a clockwise direction? Which way does the upper cross move?
5 Try adding some more crosses to the chain and mark with arrows to show the direction they would move in if one cross is turned.

Look at the two diagrams.

1 Diagram 1:
   Which way you would have to turn the handle:
   a to make the bucket move up
   b to make the bucket move down.
2 Diagram 2:
   Which way you would have to turn the handle:
   a to make the bucket move up
   b to make the bucket move down.

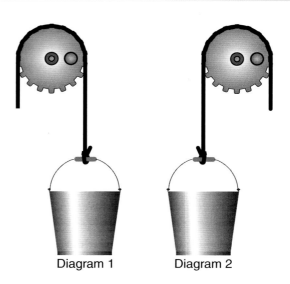

Diagram 1   Diagram 2

Look at the arrows on these cogs that are driving the bicycle chains.
Decide whether the cogs marked with a **?** are turning in a clockwise
or anti-clockwise direction.

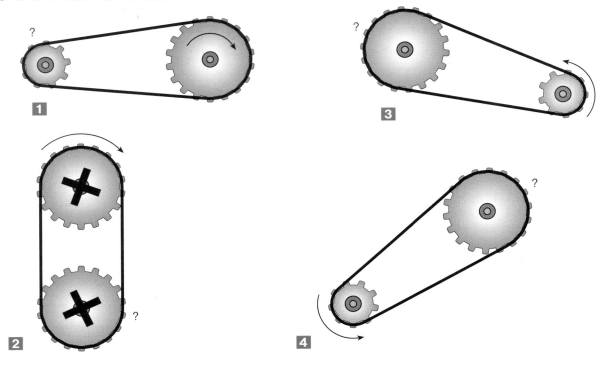

Trace these cogs, then mark with an arrow to indicate which way
each of the cogs is turning.

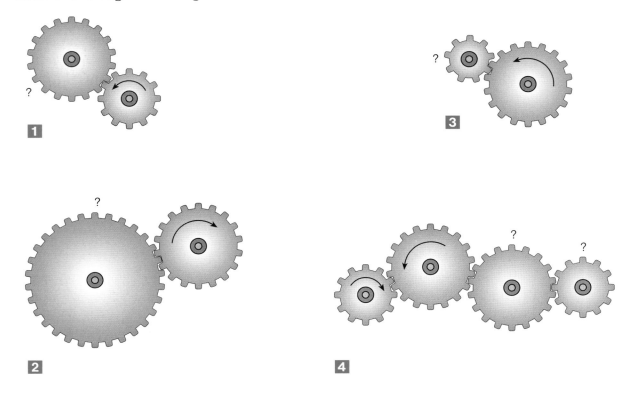

Look at these cogs. Decide in which direction they are turning.

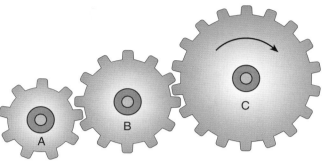

Diagram 1

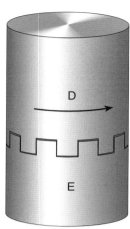

Diagram 2

1 Cog A
2 Cog B
3 Cog C
4 Cog D
5 Cog E
6 Which of the cogs rotates more times in diagram 1?
7 Which cog goes more slowly?
8 Does one cog move more slowly in diagram 2?

Now look at these cogs.

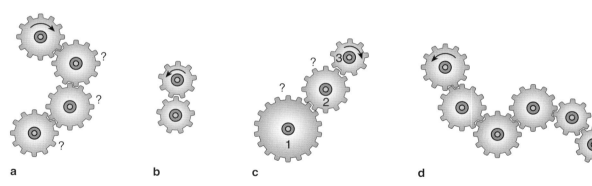

a   b   c   d

1 Trace these cogs and mark on the arrows to show which way each cog in the series is turning.
2 Look at **c**. List the cogs in order of the speed they would turn at, start with the slowest moving one.
3 What happens to the speed in diagram **b**?

Now look back on your work in this lesson.
- Why do two touching cogs turn around differently although their touching places move in one direction?
- Does a small cog turn faster than a large cog which makes it turn?

4 Shapes sliding and turning

In chess, the pieces move up, down and across on the grid. There is no need for reflection or rotation. This sliding movement of shapes is called *translation*. Do you know how shapes are reflected or rotated?

 Look at these shapes.

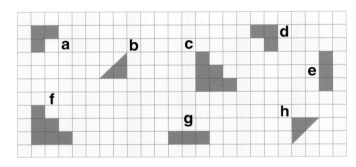

1. Match the pairs of congruent shapes.
2. Write the letters of any shapes that have slid to a new position.
3. Which shapes show reflection?
4. Have any shapes been rotated? If so, write down the letters of the shapes.

Copy these shapes and then draw the reflection. Carefully note where the mirror line is. The first one is done for you.

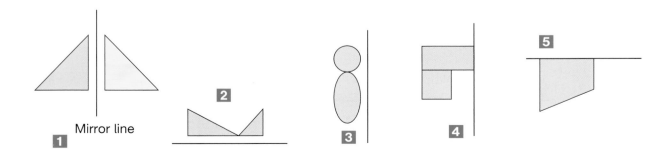

Copy these shapes on squared paper.

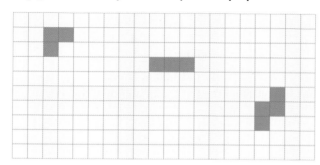

1 Choose one of the corners of the shape as a point of rotation. Write down how many times you can find a new rotation for each shape.

Copy this shape on to a piece of card. Cut it out and use it as a template.

1 Draw round the shape on to squared paper. Now slide the shape four squares to the right, and draw round it again.

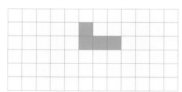

Using the same shape, each time beginning in the first position, draw round the shape again.

2 Slide the shape down two squares and draw it again.

3 Slide the shape up one square and draw its new position.

Make a template of this triangle. Mark, with a dot, the corner that is a right angle. Draw round it on squared paper, then slide it to the following positions. Count the squares from the dot on the triangle.

4 Slide the shape up three squares and draw its new position.

5 Slide the shape three squares to the right, and draw round it again.

6 Slide the shape down four squares and draw it again.

7 Move the triangle one square down, then two squares to the left.

Look at the pairs of shapes on this grid and decide whether the shapes have been reflected, slid, or rotated into their new position.

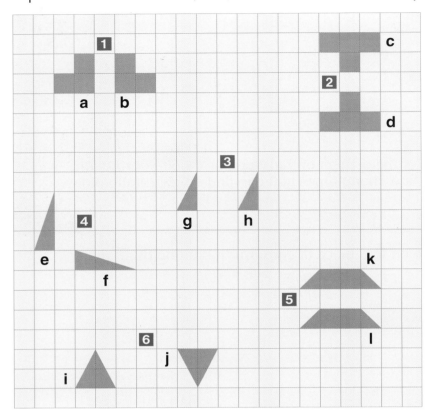

Now work these out.

1 On squared paper draw a shape of your own and draw its reflection, using the mirror lines shown.

Mirror line

Mirror line

2 Now use a different shape of your own to show how you can rotate it to different positions.

3 Draw another new shape, then slide it to three new positions. Write the instructions for the new positions, as given in exercise D.

Now look back on your work in this lesson.
- What do you need to have in order to reflect a shape?
- What do we call shapes that are the same, but in different positions or facing different directions?

⑤ Rotation symmetry

How is this pattern made?
Where can you see similar patterns?

Think about this shape and follow the instructions.

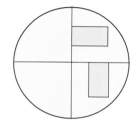

1 Use a circular protractor to make a small circular shape, or drawn round something small and circular. Mark the centre with a dot. Now put a mark every quarter-turn (90°) around the circle.

2 Cut a small rectangle from a piece of card. Now copy the design above, to show how the pattern rotates.
Write: *This design has rotational order 4.*

3 Draw another circle and split it up in the same way.

4 Now cut a new shape of your own and show rotational order 4.

Follow these instructions.

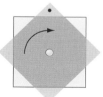 

1 Trace the square and the triangle and the hexagon shapes. Now place the tracing over the shape. Put a drawing pin in the centre of the shape. Mark one corner of the shape with a dot.

2 Now turn the tracing paper round, slowly, and see how many times you can fit the traced shape exactly over the shape on your paper. Remember you can only turn the shape through one full turn.

3 Write down the name of the shape, and record your results.

Look at these shapes. Fill in this table with the results.

Shape	Rotation order
1	
2	
3	
4	
5	
6	
7	
8	

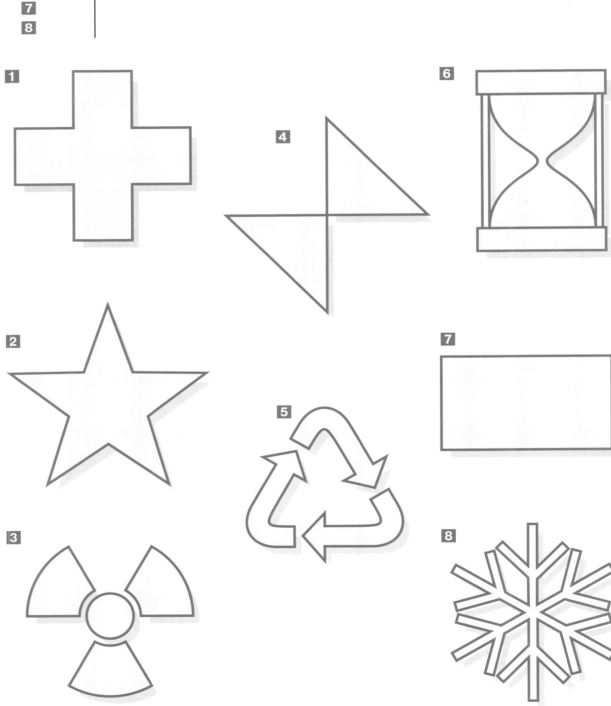

Use your circular protractor to make two circles.

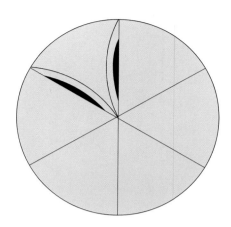 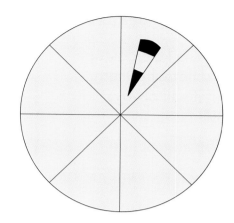

1 Mark one off in six sections (60°). Mark the second one in eight sections (45°).

2 Repeat the designs shown to show rotational order 6, and rotational order 8.

Look at these logos and decide the order of rotational symmetry.

1

3

5

2

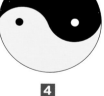

4

6

Now look back on your work in this lesson.
• Which order of rotational symmetry is the most common in familiar shapes?
• Is rotational symmetry as common in natural things as reflection symmetry?

⑥ Shape and space skills

When you shake a kaleidoscope you will get a different pattern every time, but it will always be symmetrical.

Look at this grid.

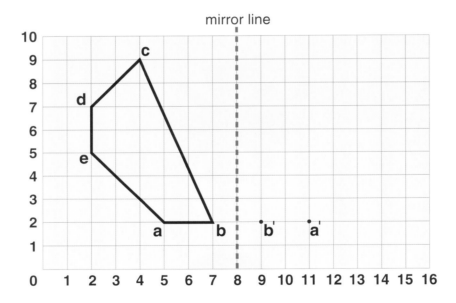

1 Write down the co-ordinates for each of the letters **a** to **e**.

Now answer these questions.

1 Copy the shape in exercise A on to squared paper, making sure the co-ordinates are correct.

2 Draw in the mirror line.

3 Now draw the reflection of this shape on your grid.

4 Give the co-ordinates of the reflected shape. Call the new corners **a′ b′** etc.

Match the pairs of congruent shapes.

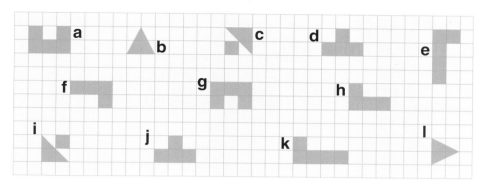

Look at the pairs of shapes you have matched together.
1. Which shapes have been reflected?
2. Which shapes have slid to a new position?
3. Which shapes show rotation?
4. Look at shapes **e** and **k**. Give the instructions to slide shape **e** to its new position of shape **k**.
5. Now give instructions to move shape **j** to its new position of shape **d**.

Look at these cogs.

Write the order of rotational symmetry for each cog.

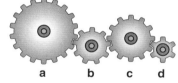

1. cog **a** =   3. cog **c** =
2. cog **b** =   4. cog **d** =

If cog **a** turns in a clockwise direction, in which direction will the other cogs move?
1. cog **b**
2. cog **c**
3. cog **d**
4. If cog **c** has 12 teeth, and cog **d** has six teeth, how many times will cog **d** rotate in one rotation of cog **c**?
5. Which cog in this series will rotate the least number of times?
6. Which cog in the series will rotate the fastest?

Now look back on your work in this lesson.
- What is common between cog movement and rotational symmetry?
- What types of movement of shapes on a grid can you name?

Module ❶5–❶8

Review your skills

Number and measurement

1 Kathy and her three friends have won £16 on the school raffle. How much will each of them get if it is shared fairly?

2 There are 20 chocolates on the top tray of a box. How many can Peter, Alex, Duncan and Penny have each if they eat the whole tray?

3 At the school fair £2 buys 12 balls for Beat the Goalie. How many shots each can four friends have for £2?

Jack is told to prepare the new reduced sale prices for these items. Here is his list of cuts to make.

a £589

b £675

£605

c

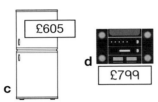
d

£799

Reduce all TVs by £86
Reduce all fridge-freezers by £64
Reduce all music centres by £91

4 What is the sale price of each item?

1	24	47
12	35	58
23	46	69

5 What is the along rule?

6 What is the down rule?

Handling data

1 Which of the following choices would give you a rough idea of what is the most popular computer game in the country?

a Ask everybody their opinion.

b Ask a sample of people of different ages.

c Ask your friends.

d Look at adverts.

2 Suppose you make a tally chart of the newspapers which 30 people usually read. A newspaper called *The Globe* has these marks against it: ̶H̶̶H̶|. What does this mean?

Think about even numbers. Now think of the numbers of the 3× table.

3 Write down ten even numbers.

4 Write down ten numbers that are in the 3× table.

5 Write down all of the numbers that are in *both* of your answers.

Number and algebra

Write down the most sensible metric measure to use for each of these measurements.

| millimetres | centimetres | metres | grams | kilograms |

1 The length of a path in the park
2 The width of the desk
3 The weight of a dog
4 The thickness of a nail
5 The weight of some sugar to add to the cake mix

Draw lines of these lengths, using your ruler.
6 4 cm
7 37 mm

Can you measure to the nearest millimetre?

8 The length of this rectangle
9 The width of this rectangle
10 Draw a rectangle twice as long but with the same width.

Shape and space

Say whether these have rotational symmetry or not.

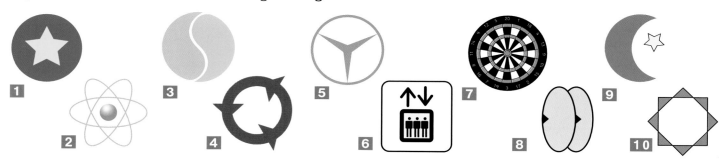

Now try this...

How many different four-cell shapes can you have? The cells must be connected along one full side at least – a corner touching is not enough. Draw the shapes and then label the shapes that are congruent, even though they look different.

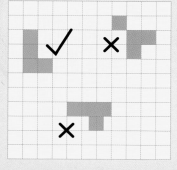

Check your skills

You can check how well you can do the things listed here. Get your parents and friends to help.

Number and algebra

1 I can solve problems using mental multiplication and division.

2 I can find how much a number is increased or decreased by using addition and subtraction, on a calculator if appropriate.

3 I can decide which of two areas is bigger, using numbers of tiles.

4 I can complete a grid from a starting entry where there are rules for the rows and columns.

Handling data

1 I understand how surveys are used in everyday life.

2 I can use a tally chart to record data in groups covering a range of numbers.

3 I can get data out of a database using the word *and*.

4 I can use two sets of data which have elements common to both.

5 I understand and can use a two-stage ordering system.

Number and measurements

1 I know and can use sizes in inches and feet.

2 I know and can use sizes in millimetres and centimetres.

3 I can use a ruler or tape marked and numbered in millimetres to make measurements.

4 I know what kind of things are weighed in ounces, pounds, stones and tons.

5 I know what kind of things are weighed in grams.

Shape and space

1 I can find and give the position of something on a grid using co-ordinate pairs.

2 I can match up congruent shapes and pictures in various positions.

3 I understand how meshed cogs turn clockwise and anti-clockwise, faster or slower.

4 I understand the ways shapes can be moved by reflection, sliding and rotating.

PORTRAIT OF

Sri Lanka

PORTRAIT OF
Sri Lanka

GEHAN DE SILVA WIJEYERATNE

NEW
HOLLAND

First published in 2007 by New Holland Publishers
London • Cape Town • Sydney • Auckland
www.newhollandpublishers.com

Garfield House, 86–88 Edgware Road, London, W2 2EA, United Kingdom

80 McKenzie Street, Cape Town, 8001, South Africa

Unit 1, 66 Gibbes Street, Chatswood, NSW 2067, Australia

218 Lake Road, Northcote, Auckland, New Zealand

ISBN 978 1 84537 252 1

Although the publishers have made every effort to ensure that information
contained in this book was meticulously researched and correct at the time of
going to press, they accept no responsibility for any inaccuracies, loss, injury or
inconvenience sustained by any person using this book as reference.

Publishing Manager: Jo Hemmings
Senior Editor: Julie Delf
Editor: Sarah Larter
Assistant Editor: Kate Parker
Designer: Gülen Shevki-Taylor
Production: Joan Woodroffe
Cartography: Bill Smuts
Index: Dorothy Frame

Reproduction by Pica Digital Pte Ltd
Printed and bound in Malaysia by Tien Wah Press (Pte) Ltd

10 9 8 7 6 5 4 3 2 1

HALF TITLE PAGE *A traditional bullock cart still in use for carting goods,
at Sigiriya.*

TITLE PAGES (LEFT) *An elaborately decorated elephant in the Diya
Kapana ceremony of the annual* Esala Perahera *(Pageant).*

(RIGHT)*A fire dancer swirls a wheel of flames during the annual* Esala
Perahera *(Pageant).*

CONTENTS PAGE *Dancers representing the Veddas, the aboriginal
people of Sri Lanka, at the Diya Kapana ceremony.*

THIS PAGE *Two ladies cross a paddy field from their village to reach a
principal road.*

CONTENTS

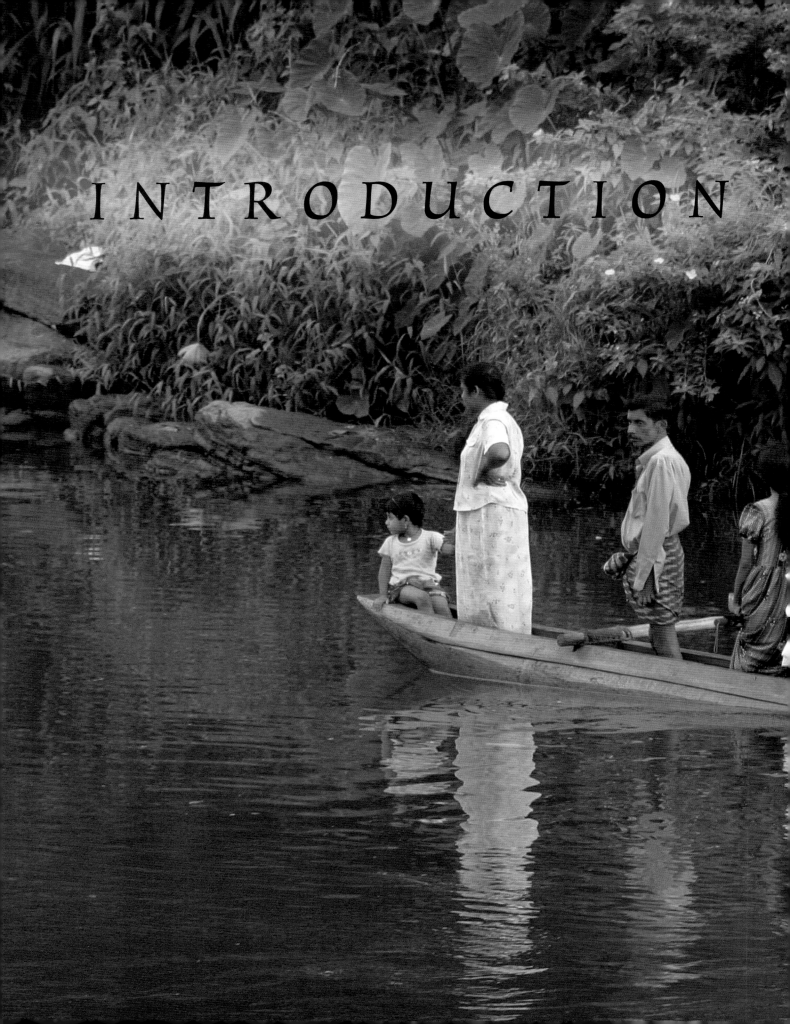

INTRODUCTION

INTRODUCTION

An Ancient History

Sri Lanka's official history begins in the 5th century BC, with the arrival of Prince Vijaya. The prince was rebellious and ill-disciplined, and his father banished him from his kingdom in northern India as a punishment for his bad behaviour. Vijaya and the 700 followers who were expelled with him landed on the island of Sri Lanka, where he befriended Kuveni, a sorceress from a local tribe called the Yakkas. With Kuveni's help, Vijaya defeated the Yakkas and established his kingdom. It is quite likely that the fable of Vijaya is a metaphorical account of the waves of immigrants that came from north and south India and integrated with the local population.

The ancient city of Anuradhapura was reportedly founded by one of the Vijaya's generals, Anuradha. In the 4th century BC, King Pandukabaya (c. 437–367 BC) made it his capital and began a number of important irrigation works. The city reached its zenith in the 6th century, and it continued to be the most dominant and powerful city on the island for many centuries.

But Anuradhapura's wealth attracted the envy and greed of successive invaders from India. In the 11th century AD, successive waves of Chola invaders from India prompted the capital to be moved to Polonnaruwa, with brief interludes at Yapahuwa and Dambadeniya. During the reign of Parakramabahu (1153–86), known as 'the Great', the city expanded. He was an enthusiastic patron of the arts and an accomplished 'tank' (reservoir) builder. The stone sculptures at Gal Vihara, which were built during his reign, have a scale, subtlety and finesse that is not seen anywhere else in the world. Polonnaruwa grew into a city that rivalled Anuradhapura, but it was eventually sacked by invaders and the capital shifted to Kandy in the hills.

ABOVE *The* Mahavamsa, *compiled in the 5th Century AD, records events from 543 BC to 310 AD. The* Mahavansa *recorded in writing details of history which had been passed down in the oral tradition. Inscriptions such as this stone tablet in Polonnaruwa serve to corroborate or add new knowledge to what has been documented in the* Mahavansa.

PREVIOUS PAGES *Villagers cross the Kelani River at Kithulgala in a canoe operated by the local ferry man. This picture epitomizes the rural nature of much of Sri Lanka, although it is easily overlooked by the more visible face of modernisation.*

RIGHT ABOVE AND BELOW *The Mirror Wall at Sigiriya is built against a sheer rock face. After the citadel was abandoned, it attracted visitors, who have been described as amongst the earliest recorded tourists. These visitors used the polished surface for scribbling their thoughts, often in the form of poems. Many are artistic in content, but some provide an insight into the past.*

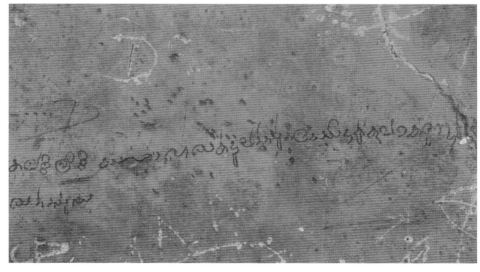

The Colonial Era

The new threat came not from the Indian mainland, but much further away – Europe, from where men came in search of spices and fortunes. In 1505 the Portuguese arrived when Lorenzo de Almeida accidentally drifted into the southern harbour of Galle, an event that marked the beginning of a period of European colonization of the island. The Portuguese subsequently established forts and settlements along the coastline and waged war with the Kandyan kings. In the 17th century, one of these kings, Sri Rajasinghe II, courted the help of the Dutch, whose East India Company (VOC) was actively engaged in the spice trade. With these new allies, the Portuguese were repelled – although one European power was simply replaced with another. Before long the two allies were at war.

This conflict continued for over a century until the British arrived. The British repeated history, acting as an ally of the king and driving out the Dutch, before staking their own claim to the island. The British were master tacticians and employed a policy of 'divide and rule'. They waited patiently until internal dissent boiled over under the ruthless and ill-tempered King Sri Vikrama Rajasingha. Some of the monarch's most important chieftains mutinied against him and worked with the British to capture him.

BELOW *Much of the colonial heritage which remains is British. However, in Galle and Matara the Dutch have left a visible record of their former presence in the fortifications and buildings of the 'Dutch Forts' built by them. The Galle Fort carries the emblem of the VOC or the Dutch East India Company.*

OPPOSITE ABOVE *The Dutch Reform Church, in the Galle Fort, is one of the lasting legacies of the Dutch colonial era. Recently refurbished, it remains in active use with mass on Sundays.*

OPPOSITE BELOW *Cricket and education are two of the most enduring legacies of the British colonial era. The British left behind many fine schools in Sri Lankan cities endowed with generously sized playing fields for that English obsession, cricket. St Joseph's College in Colombo is one such example with a long tradition of sport and education.*

The Plantation Economy

Under the British, Sri Lanka developed a strong economy that was based on plantations. The rainforests that clad the hillsides were cleared, driving hundreds of species unique to the islands to extinction before science could classify them. Fortunately, under the advice of the famous 19th-century botanist Joseph Hooker (1817–1911), the colonial government decreed that all of the remaining forest above an altitude of 1,500 metres (5,000 feet) should be retained to provide a watershed. Thanks to this decision, the island still has a precious remnant of its cloud forest, which is best seen at Horton Plains National Park (see page 109).

The British cleared the mountains to plant coffee. However, coffee blight destroyed the plantations and the industry collapsed in 1867. Subsequently, James Taylor introduced tea as an alternative crop. The British planters included some very famous personalities such as Sir Samuel Baker, who recounted his experiences in his book *Eight years in Ceylon*.

BELOW *The forests of the highlands were felled over a century ago for a green carpet of tea. Sri Lanka remains one of the world's largest exporters of tea.*

RIGHT The British planters imported labour from India to work on the tea plantations. These people have stayed on for generations and their descendants still work on tea plantations. Tea plucking has been difficult to mechanize and the preferred method is still to pluck by hand. The plucking is almost always done by these Tamil women of Indian descent.

RIGHT *The British planters imported labour from India to work on the tea plantations. These people have stayed on for generations and their descendants still work on tea plantations. Tea plucking has been difficult to mechanize and the preferred method is still to pluck by hand. The plucking is almost always done by these Tamil women of Indian descent.*

Baker was one of the early breed of great African explorers and famous for discovering the source of the White Nile. He also wrote a number of books and received a Gold Medal from the Royal Geographical Society.

The British also played a key role in modernizing the country. They introduced the British system of law and order, an efficient civil administration and roads and railroads were built.

THE WEST

THE WEST

Colombo

Colombo, the business capital and the most important city in Sri Lanka, is situated in the west of the island. The city has wetlands at the edges of its suburbs and rainforests just over an hour's drive away. Many of Sri Lanka's important beach resorts, such as Beruwela and Bentota, are also in this region. The west of the island provides dramatic contrasts, featuring traffic jams, sandy beaches, pristine rainforests and acres of paddy fields. Colombo is a mixed bag of a city. An urbane and sophisticated city set divides its time between classical concerts and business lunches, while the rest of the inhabitants sweat it out in what is increasingly becoming another traffic-congested Asian business metropolis. The city has a fascinating history, with its modern origins in European military outposts, which were strategically sited close to the mouth of the Kelani River to protect the lucrative spice trade.

Traces of the city's colonial past are still visible in many of its buildings and in the few road names that survived a period of nationalistic fervour that attempted to erase all evidence of the colonial period.

Despite its clear business focus, Colombo is not culturally bankrupt. On the contrary, most of the nation's important contemporary art collections are sited here. The Bellanwila and Kelaniya temples are in Colombo's suburbs, areas that have more in common with rural village life than the frenetic business centres of Fort and Pettah. Although most of the marshlands have been drained and destroyed, those that are left are being protected, a measure that will

PREVIOUS PAGES The Roman style Town Hall in Colombo was built in 1928 by a British mayor. Its architecture mirrors the White House in Washington.

LEFT The Hatton National Bank's tower block in Slave Island dominates the area. Businesses are moving out of the Fort area because of congestion and escalating real estate prices. Slave Island could develop into a new commercial hub.

save the city from flooding and provide valuable refuges for wildlife at Talangama, Kotte, Bellanwila Attidiya and Muthurajawela.

After Sri Lanka gained its independence from the British in 1948, Colombo continued to remain as its capital. In the 1980s, Sri Jayawardhanapura, on the outskirts of the city, was declared the official political capital. Despite much new development, several grand old buildings and houses still remain in Colombo. The financial and business areas of Fort and Pettah tend to be busy and crowded, as can be expected of any business district. The Cinnamon Gardens area (Colombo 7) remains exclusive, and it is the address of many diplomatic residences.

As prices of land in Colombo continue to rocket, more and more people are buying houses in the suburbs. To cater to this outflow of people, petrol sheds, supermarkets and banks are springing up in suburbs, which only a decade ago were as quiet as villages.

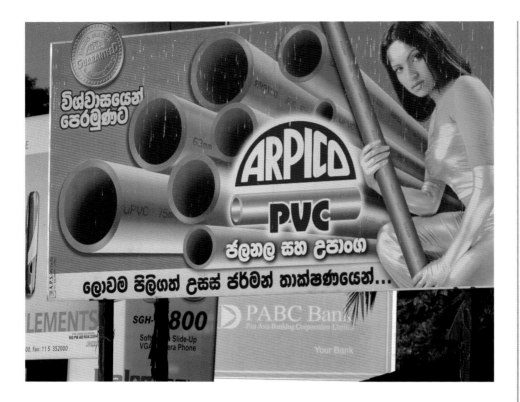

LEFT ABOVE *Advertising on bill boards has seen a surge in recent years. Larger than life advertisements are springing up at busy junctions to catch the eye of commuters who are a captive audience in the rush hour.*

LEFT BELOW *The Colombo Fort area still sports a combination of the old and the new. The twin towers of the World Trade Center stand juxtaposed against the British colonial façade of the York Building.*

National Museum

The National Museum in Colombo, usually referred to as the Colombo Museum, is housed in a grand old colonial building built by Arasy Marikar Wapuche Marikar, an architect of Moorish descent. The museum was commissioned during the governorship of Sir William Gregory (1817–92). Gregory, a member of the British Parliament, was a campaigner and patron of the arts, he was also one of the first to lobby for the British Museum in London to be open on a Sunday for the benefit of the general public. The Colombo Museum was declared open on the 1st January 1877. However, the nucleus of its collection had been laid down 30 years previously in the private collections of the members of the Ceylon Branch of the Royal Asiatic Society. The museum has sunk into neglect in recent years, but in 2005, with private sector participation, some of its exhibits were modernized. It contains one of the finest collections of Sri Lankan cultural artefacts. Situated behind the National Museum is the Natural History Museum.

RIGHT ABOVE *A sculpture of a Bodhisattva Avalokiteshvara in the National Museum, Colombo. The style of the sculpture shows affinities to works from South India in the 7th-9th centuries.*

RIGHT BELOW *The National Museum, Colombo on Sir Marcus Fernando Mawatha is one of the most attractive buildings in Colombo from the colonial era. It is surrounded by spacious lawns.*

Colombo at Leisure

If Kandy remains the centre of the classical arts, Colombo is a melting pot where westernized Sri Lankans rub shoulders with those who remain very conservative in outlook. As with many cities, the modern arts seem to gain more media attention over the classical arts. Colombo tends to dominate the *avant garde* of the arts whether it is in painting, sculpture, theatre or dance. Despite a pronounced effort to hold international fixtures in other major cities, Colombo gains the lion's share of fixtures with any visiting sports team, troupe of dancers or musicians. Despite a relatively modest infrastructure of purpose-built facilities for the arts and sports, there is always something happening in Colombo. Classical music (Sri Lankan and Western), poetry readings, jazz festivals, stage theatre, sporting fixtures, etc. occur on an almost daily basis, providing something for everyone.

Colombo is also becoming more conscious of the need for leisure spaces. The Galle Face Green adjoining the sea, Vihara Maha Devi Park and the new Parliament Grounds are some of the most popular. The zoo is always very busy during the weekends. Shopping malls are also increasingly becoming hubs for leisure activity as shopping in the capital follows the global trend of being a leisure pursuit.

BELOW *Colombo is the venue for many sports fixtures, including cricket. Sport is becoming increasingly professional and corporations are now investing serious money in sponsorship. This helps to raise the profile of both the sport and the players.*

ABOVE *Ananda Coomaraswamy Mawatha more aptly described by its previous colonial name of Greenpath, has evolved into a open air venue for artisans. A mixture of styles from classical to all manners of modern art is present.*

RIGHT *Galle Face Green, is not so green any more as the turf is under pressure from city dwellers who crowd it on evenings and during week-ends. Kite flying is a popular pastime on the Green and the Green hosts an annual kite flying festival.*

23

Flowering Trees of Colombo

Colombo has its share of shortcomings. Traffic congestion, unsightly rubbish, pollution etc. Nevertheless, Colombo is also a veritable garden city. Its streets are lined with ancient trees which are ageing gracefully. The city fathers regularly plant new trees to replenish those which fall with every monsoon. House-proud owners manicure and tend garden plots on the roadside, even though it is on public land. Corporations sponsor the small island gardens at roundabouts. Some of the city's five-star hotels have allocated generous space to lush tropical gardens. Although the emergence of a condominium culture is inevitable, Colombo still has many houses with sizeable gardens which provide a habitat for birds, butterflies, dragonflies, lizards and a host of other animals. Seen from a high roof top, most people are struck by the abundance of tropical foliage.

In May and June, Colombo undergoes a dramatic flowering. Species of *Cassias* and *Tabebuias* in pink, *Erythrinas* and the magnificent Flamboyant in red, the Yellow Silk Cotton and the Yellow Flames bedecked in yellow, the Queen's Flower in purple and a host of other

BELOW *The Jacaranda (*Jacaranda mimosaefolia*) is a fairly inconspicuous tree with spindly branches and feathery leaves. During the flowering season it is transformed with purple flowers on spikes.*

RIGHT ABOVE *Guildford Crescent in Colombo houses the Lionel Wendt Art Center, which has seen many a flowering of theatrical and artistic talent. It is also a beautiful tree-lined avenue which blooms seasonally with a flush of pink* Tabebuias *and the purple clusters of the Queen's Flower (*Lagerstroemia speciosa*).*

RIGHT BELOW *The Indian Coral Tree (*Erythrina variegata*) is often seen in a flush of red during the flowering season on estates in the country and in towns. Its claw shaped red flowers and triangular leaves are distinctive.*

trees put out flowers. But almost all of these flowering trees, are trees introduced to Sri Lanka during colonial times. Some come from as far away as Mexico and others from closer such as mainland India or South-east Asia.

Buddhism

During the 3rd century BC, one of the most momentous events in the cultural history of the island took place – Buddhism was introduced. King Asoka of India (c. 273–232 BC) had embraced Buddhism and sent priests all over the world to convert others to the philosophy. His son, Mahinda Thera, arrived on the island and encountered King Devanampiyatissa (307–247 BC) out hunting at Mihintale. The king was surprised and indignant to hear someone calling out his first name. Looking around, he saw Mahinda, who asked him a riddle, which the king answered correctly. It is perhaps one of the earliest records of a person being subjected to an IQ test before time was invested in converting and grooming that individual for a mission. Satisfied with the king's intelligence, Mahinda preached the tenets of Buddhsim to the monarch, who was converted. The king declared that no more hunting would take place at Mihintale, making it the oldest wildlife sanctuary on historical record.

BELOW *Pandols are a vivid and glorious celebration of the Buddha and his teachings. Painted panels depict events from his previous lives and the lessons to be learnt. At night they are lit with hundreds of electric bulbs and crowds gather to listen to prayers.*

RIGHT *Days of the full moon ('Poya' days) are public holidays in Sri Lanka. They are considered holy as the Buddha was born, attained enlightenment (Nirvana) and passed away on a full moon day. Some Poya days are more important than others and the most important is that of Vesak which marks the birth, enlightenment and passing away of the Buddha. Temples are decorated with the Buddhist flag and people gather to celebrate.*

Vesak

Vesak commemorates the day of the birth of Prince Siddhartha of India, his enlightenment as a Buddha and his passing away. The celebration takes place in May on the day of a full moon. It is the most important date in the Buddhist calendar. The development of Vesak as a day of celebration, during which the streets are decorated with lanterns, has a fairly recent history. In the 19th century, an American named Henry Olcott (1832–1907) converted to Buddhism and worked towards upholding and promoting the traditions of the religion. He wanted to give Buddhists a national day that was the equivalent of the Christian Christmas and came up with the concept of Vesak. Rather than cutting trees, Olcott proposed the creation of paper lanterns, which are lit at night. The lanterns have a philosophical significance, symbolizing the power of light to dispel darkness.

Today, Vesak has become one of the biggest national festivals in Asia. All over Sri Lanka people make Vesak lanterns and hang them over doorways and along the streets. Numerous local competitions are held for the creation of the most beautiful Vesak lanterns. Gigantic podiums called pandols are constructed on streets. They are lit up with hundreds of electric bulbs that illuminate panels showing scenes from the *Jataka Tales*, which tell the stories of the Buddha's previous births, before attaining Nirvana. Although Vesak is celebrated all over the island, Colombo is one of the best places in which to observe the festivities.

OPPOSITE *Vesak Day is marked by Vesak lantern building competitions all over the island. Some of the grandest competitions are held in Colombo with entire streets designated as exhibition venues. Winning entries are usually the product of a team of artisans.*

BELOW *Devotees light lamps on a Vesak Poya. Lamps are lit as an act of piety. To avoid damage to temple murals many temples now have racks outside for placing lamps and forbid the lighting of lamps inside the temples.*

LEFT *Sir Henry Olcott introduced the idea of building Vesak lanterns as a symbol of light against the darkness of ignorance. Temples, households and commercial buildings are decorated with lanterns during Vesak.*

BELOW *A line of women listen to* Pirith, *Buddhist prayers being chanted at the famous Bellanwila temple on the outskirts of Colombo. The more conservative or traditionally minded ladies will dress in pure white when visiting a temple and especially so if they are visiting on a Poya day to observe* Sil.

RIGHT *A young girl dressed in a* lama sari, *on Vesak Poya at the Bellanwila temple. Young girls wear this special, elegant dress when visiting the temple for religious observances or Sunday School.*

The Kelaniya Temple

The Kelaniya Temple, or *vihara*, has been in existence since ancient times. *The Sinhalese Chronicles*, which are historical records of the island, state that it was built by King Yatala Tissa. But this is disputed in a later chronicle, the *Pujavaliya*, which attributes the founding of the *vihara* to King Kavan Tissa of the Ruhuna kingdom in the south. There is no clear evidence for either version and so the founder of this wonderful *vihara* remains a mystery.

It is recorded that in the 6th century BC Lord Buddha visited Kelaniya to stop two rival Naga clans from fighting over a gem-studded golden chain. The Buddha settled their dispute and they presented a chair to him. This chair is said to have been placed in the present *dagaba*, a shrine for Buddhist relics. In the early part of the 2nd century BC, Yattala Tissa, who ruled from Kelaniya, sent his only daughter floating out to sea in a boat as penance for having killed a monk. The boat landed at Kirinda, where she became the queen of Kavan Tissa of Magama, now known as Tissamaharama. This legend is now believed to tell the story of a tsunami.

LEFT *A Buddhist nun in thoughtful repose at the Kelaniya Temple. Buddhist nuns or bhikkunis are not in the public eye like their male counterparts. They do not conduct prayer ceremonies or other rituals. In the Buddhist clergy, the power and influence lies with the* bhikkus *or male Buddhist monks.*

The Princess of the Tsunami went on to become the most famous mother of Sri Lanka, Queen Vihara Maha Devi. Her son, Prince Dutugemunu fought and defeated the Indian invader Elara at Anuradhapura and reunited Sri Lanka under one king.

ABOVE *On special days such as Poya, the white stupas at temples may be decorated with the Buddhist flag.*

RIGHT *An elderly Buddhist nun, dressed in a vibrantly coloured robe, prays fervently.*

ABOVE *The Ganas or dwarf-like mythical creatures are a favourite iconic element in decorative friezes in classical buildings. It is not unusual to find them portrayed with a sense of comic mischief.*

LEFT *Devotees make offering of burning incense sticks in front of figures of the Buddha. The perfume and smoke adds a heady atmosphere.*

OPPOSITE *A relief of Vishnu on one of the walls of the Kelaniya Temple shows the deity in a Karanda-makuta head dress. The front right arm is in an Abhaya-mudra posture and the front left arm is in a Varada-mudra posture. The sculpture is a 1920s interpretation of a classical figure which has been sensitively moulded with the various iconographic details within the frame of a Makara thorana (a decorative detail symbolizing a dragon).*

Talangama Wetland

This wetland on the outskirts of Colombo is bordered by main roads, which means that access is easy for wildlife enthusiasts. The complex of ponds, canals and paddy fields, makes it a rich and varied wetland site. Many common wetland birds can be seen and over 100 species have been recorded here. Highlights include the Watercock and migrant Black and Yellow Bitterns. The Purple-faced Leaf Monkey, a critically endangered sub-species that is endemic to Sri Lanka, is also found here. Talangama is also excellent for spotting butterflies and dragonflies.

LEFT *A Pheasant-tailed Jacana (*Hydrophasianus chirurgus*) treads delicately on water lilies on the main lake at Talangama. During the breeding season the birds develop their long tails and a golden hind neck. Their unusually long toes help to distribute their weight, enabling them to walk on lily pads.*

OPPOSITE *The surface of lily pads contain a waxy coating or pruinescence which result in globules of water forming after rain.*

LEFT *In wetlands such as Talangama, the local people harvest the flowers and the root tubers of the lilies.*

Dragonflies

About 117 species of dragonfly and damselfly have been recorded on the island, of which an astonishing 52 species are endemic (found nowhere else in the world). The presence of so many unique dragonflies and damselflies means that they are extremely important in the study of Sri Lanka's biodiversity. Some species found in recent years still await description, and it is quite likely that many additional insects from this family are yet to be recorded and described. The excitement of describing new species is only dampened by the realization that the island may have lost many species before botanists could record them. The larvae of all dragonflies and damselflies are known as nymphs and lead an aquatic existence. Consequently, the survival of these insects depends on the presence of a suitable environment in the vicinity of a healthy aquatic habitat. This reliance on fresh water means that dragonfly species are good indicators of the quality of an ecosystem, in much the same way as other groups, such as birds, can be used to assess the degree to which a habitat has been disturbed.

A species such as the Variable Colourwing is quite resilient and can often be seen on polluted canals and waterways. In contrast, the Shining Gossamerwing, although not rare, is most likely to be seen in natural, relatively undisturbed forested streams. Sri Lanka's wetlands, such as that at Talangama, are excellent places to become acquainted with the more common species.

A wetland such as Talangama will hold over 20 species of dragonfly in a variety of habitats including ditches, ponds, reedbeds, open lakes and paddy fields. The diversity of species is a measure of the richness of matrix of habitats at a particular site.

OPPOSITE *Black Velvet-wing* (Neurothemia tullia) *is one of the commonest dragonflies found in the wet zone lowlands. The adult is strikingly coloured. When the dragonflies emerge, they spread, at times even venturing into gardens in towns, in search of suitable habitat.*

RIGHT ABOVE *The Spine-legged Reedling* (Rhodothemis rufa) *likes to perch on the stems of stiff reeds next to large ponds or lakes. It can easily be confused with the similar Eastern Scarlet Darter* (Crocothemis servilia).

RIGHT BELOW *Variable Basker* (Urothemis signata) *is another dragonfly which likes vegetation besides ponds. The juveniles and females are drably coloured in relation to the red male.*

Village Life

Over 90 per cent of Sri Lanka's population of 20 million people inhabit rural areas. The lifestyles of the busy cities of Colombo, Kandy, Galle, Matara and their ilk are a far cry from the lifestyles enjoyed by the majority of the population. In the last three decades, vast improvements have been made to provide running water, schools and electricity to the rural populace. The new challenge is to create employment.

The traditional village of Sri Lanka's interior had three elements: an irrigation lake or a system of lakes, paddy fields downstream and a village temple. The lakes were part of a cascade system, which was cleverly placed along hydraulic gradients to maximize rainwater accumulation and retain a high water table. Village life in many areas of the island continues as it has done for centuries, although with some minor changes. Farmers who traditionally wore sarongs during the day are now seen in shirts and long trousers. However, before the seasonal rains arrive, they will wear a strip of cloth wrapped around their legs, known as an *amudaya*. With their *amudayas* on, they set forth to plough the paddy fields.

Village life has a degree of civil order which is more sophisticated than an outsider might suspect. The farmers in particular are well organised into local collectives of Govi Samagamas or Farmers' Societies. They lobby the local authorities and national departments such as the Irrigation Department to ensure that their basic needs are met. The farmers are increasingly acquiring a leaning towards being an environmental lobby. Through generations of experience they understand that if wetlands are drained and filled up, it creates problems with flooding as the natural sponge which soaked up storm water is absent. The farmers understand the need for environmental safeguards and also the need to keep open lands for aesthetic reasons. Any efforts to convert paddy land is resisted by the farmers' collectives.

RIGHT *Traditional mud huts in Sri Lanka are often completed with a coconut thatch roof. The leaves are dried, soaked and woven to create the ubiquitous covering that can be found in much of Sri Lanka and India.*

LEFT *A villager in Talangama carries plants, attired in a traditional sarong. The old villagers co-exist with a new breed of city professionals who have discovered Talangama.*

OPPOSITE BELOW *A typical rural food stall selling fruit. Despite the growth of supermarkets, stalls such as this still hold their own.*

ABOVE *Terraced paddy fields in Sri Lanka are protected and by law cannot be converted for any other purpose. This allows the traditional farming cycle to be maintained in perpetuity in the village paddy fields which still adjoin Colombo. Paddy fields are increasingly becoming important habitats for some wildlife, as urbanization spreads around the capital.*

Sinharaja Rainforest

The Sinharaja Man and Biosphere Reserve was declared a World Heritage Site in 1988. It is arguably the most important biodiversity site in Sri Lanka and is also an important international tropical biodiversity site.

Sinharaja comprises of lowland and sub-montane wet evergreen forests with sub-montane Patana grasslands in the east. A staggering 64 per cent of the tree species are endemic to Sri Lanka. The lower slopes and valleys have a remnant of *Dipterocarpus* forest, with the middle and higher slopes characterized by trees of the genus *Mesua*. Orchids and Pitcher Plants are common on nutrient poor soils.

Many of Sri Lanka's endemic birds can be seen here, among which are the Red-faced Malkoha, Green-billed Coucal, Serendib Scops Owl, Chestnut-backed Owlet, Spot-winged Thrush, Ceylon Rufous Babbler, Ashy-headed Laughing-Thrush, Ceylon Blue Magpie, White-faced Starling, Ceylon Hill-Myna, Ceylon Scaly Thrush and Ceylon Crested Drongo. Species that also inhabit the Indian subcontinent include the Malabar Trogon and Ceylon Frogmouth.

Half of Sri Lanka's endemic mammals and butterflies are present. A few Leopards are also present but the visitor is more likely to see Purple-faced Leaf Monkey and Grizzled Indian Squirrel. Otters have been seen in the paddy fields north of the guards' hut at the start of the old logging road. A night walk might produce a Red Loris. Endemic lizards include the endangered Whistling Lizard and Rough-nosed Horned Lizard. Threatened freshwater fish include Combtail, Smooth-breasted Snakehead, Black Ruby Barb, Cherry Barb, and Red-tail Goby.

A butterfly regularly encountered in Sinharaja is the endemic Tree Nymph. It floats overhead, as if it was a piece of light, tissue paper, caught in the breeze. The Commander is another regular, flying with a stiff, hunched action. A flash of colour on the logging road might reveal a host of Whites and Sulphurs mud sipping. The Painted Saw-tooth, a scarce, beautiful butterfly may be amongst them.

ABOVE *Epiphytes cloak a tree. In a rainforest, all plants are in competition for light. Epiphytes grow on other plants and cheat by getting to the top without having to invest in their own trunk to carry leaves.*

LEFT *Different plants have different growth strategies in a rainforest. Climbers use the trunk of another to support their bid to reach the canopy where levels of light are higher.*

RIGHT *As many as 80 per cent or more of Sri Lanka's land snails may be found nowhere else in the world. Although not glamorous, land snails can provide important clues to processes of climate change and evolutionary change.*

*The Green Garden Lizard (*Calotes calotes*) is confined to Sri Lanka and India. Breeding males turn their heads into a bright crimson when they are courting females or fending off rival males.*

Several hundred species of fungi are found in Sri Lanka. They play an important part in decomposing dead plant and animal matter and in helping to recycle nutrients efficiently in the rainforest.

Endemic Birds

The presence of a number of birds endemic to Sri Lanka results in birdwatchers coming from all over the world especially to see them. A specialist eco-tourism industry has developed to cater to these enthusiasts. The rainforests on the west of the island, such as Sinharaja, provide a good opportunity for birdwatchers to see these remarkable species.

Many of Sri Lanka's bird species are shared with the Indian subcontinent. This is probably because much of the lowlands, in particular the northern half of the island, split from India relatively recently in geological terms. The southern half of the island is believed to have been contiguous with the Western Ghats of India, and is thought to have been isolated from the mainland for a long enough time for distinct species to evolve. Most of Sri Lanka's endemic fauna and flora is contained within the southern half of the island, in the wet, western sector and highlands in the central mountain massif. No less than 33 species of bird are considered to be endemic to Sri Lanka. Among them is the Serendib Scops-Owl, a species that was discovered as recently as in 2001 by Deepal Warakagoda.

In a lowland rainforest like Sinharaja, birdwatchers can see all but a handful of the 33 endemic birds. Despite Sinharaja's importance, the road access and facilities remain very basic.

BELOW *The Red-faced Malkoha (*Phaenicophaeus pyrrhocephalus) *is one of the rarest endemic birds of Sri Lanka. It is confined to a few remaining rainforests such as Sinharaja, Morapitiya and Kithulgala.*

ABOVE *The endemic Ceylon Hanging Parrot (*Loriculus beryllinus*) is widespread in the lowlands and hills. It is hard to see as it frequents tree tops.*

RIGHT ABOVE *The endemic Ceylon Wood-Shrike (*Tephrodornis affinis*) is often seen and heard in the scrub forests of the dry lowlands.*

RIGHT BELOW *The endemic Ceylon Grey Hornbill (*Ocyceros gingalensis*) is found wherever suitable pockets of wooded habitat remain. The male (shown) has more extensive yellow on the bill.*

51

ABOVE *Described to science only in 2004, the endemic Serendib Scops-owl (Otus thilohoffmanni) overturned the belief that Sri Lanka's birds were well known and no new species awaited discovery.*

RIGHT *Found in many forest patches of any significant size in the wet zone, is the endemic Spot-winged Ground-thrush (Zoothera spiloptera). It feeds on the forest floor.*

LEFT *Sinharaja, Morapitiya, Kithulgala and Bodhinagala are amongst the few remaining rainforests in which the endangered endemic Green-billed Coucal (*Centropus chlororhynchos) *is still found.*

Bodhinagala Rainforest

Bodhinagala is a relatively small tract of secondary lowland rainforest, with a Buddhist hermitage located centrally. It is surprisingly rich in flora, and is also home to a number of endemic fauna. The forest is within relatively easy reach of Colombo.

Bodhinagala's claim to fame with bird lovers, is as a reliable site to spot the Green-billed Coucal. A number of other endemic species, such as the Ceylon Spurfowl, Yellow-fronted Barbet, Ceylon Small Barbet, Black-capped Bulbul, Spot-winged Thrush, along with subcontinental species such as the Ceylon Frogmouth and Malabar Trogon are visible here. Butterflies that may be seen include the Tawny Rajah. The endemic Purple-faced Leaf Monkey, Toque Monkey and Grizzled Indian Squirrel are among the mammals to watch out for.

RIGHT *The tender leaves of rainforest plants are often red because of a lack of chlorophyll. It can also serve as a signal that the young leaves are packed with un-palatable alkaloids.*

OPPOSITE ABOVE *Thebu* (Costus speciosus) *is found in shaded forests in Sri Lanka and mainland Asia. Its rhizome is used for treating fever.*

OPPOSITE BELOW *The Black-backed Dwarf Kingfisher* (Ceyx erithaca erithacus) *is not especially rare. But its discreet habits, small size and occupation of dimly lit wet zone forests means it is seldom seen by many.*

NORTH OF
COLOMBO

NORTH OF COLOMBO

The journey north of Colombo takes you out of the humid, wet region and into the dry lowlands that abut the north-central plains, an area rich in archaeological sites. Close to the capital's airport is Negombo, a rapidly growing town, which is bordered by a cluster of fishing villages. The beaches here are some of the finest and widest in the country. Further north, the Kalpitiya Peninsula remains fairly undeveloped, although its beauty has been spoiled by the prawn farms that have ravaged the once extensive mangroves. Wilpattu National Park and the Annaiwilundawa Wetland remain within a day trip's range for holidaymakers staying in resorts such as Negombo.

Negombo – a Fishing Community

The coastline of Sri Lanka is dotted with fishing communities. The beach hotels in Negombo provide very convenient access to many of these. The fishing industry is one of the key activities of the area north of Colombo, providing employment and contributing to the local

PREVIOUS PAGES *A 'coconut belt' runs northwards from Negombo through to Chilaw. Sri Lanka is one of the key producers of coconuts in the world, but much of the crop is consumed at home.*

BELOW *Fishermen pulling in their nets are a common sight on the beaches of Sri Lanka. Although motorized boats are increasingly common, traditional methods have not been lost.*

economy. Traditional fishing villages are still found everywhere on the coast. Some fishermen are nomadic, moving between one area and another, depending on the prevailing monsoon, and setting up temporary coastal villages called *wadiyas*. Most fishing villages, however, are permanent.

A gradual process of mechanization has been introduced by Sri Lanka's Fisheries Department, aided by various foreign donor programmes, with the aim of improving the yield and efficiency of the fleets. In harbours such as Beruwela and Negombo, many of the

ABOVE (TOP) *Dragging the catch has been a communal activity from time immemorial in fishing villages. Helpers are given a share of the catch.* (BOTTOM) *To make karola or dried fish, the fish are dried out in the sun. Although strong in odour when raw, when fried the karola loses its odour and is tasty.*

boats are now powered by outboard motors. But catamarans using sails to harness the wind are still seen berthing on the beach at Negombo. Even with these traditional craft, subtle modernization has taken place, as some of the wooden hulls have been replaced by fibreglass hulls.

The motor-powered boats and catamarans that do not venture into the open ocean cast nets offshore. The boats usually return to land early in the morning, the fish picked from the nets by hand and loaded into buckets. The crew and those who help them unload their catches receive a share of the fish. The rest is sold by auction to the small wholesalers who gather around the boats to haggle and strike deals. Larger fish may be cut into pieces by a fishmonger on the spot or taken away in refrigerated vans by the larger wholesalers.

Those who fancy buying their sea food fresh can engage in a spot of friendly bargaining. Prawns and cuttlefish can be bought at amazing discounts to street retail prices.

LEFT *Being a tropical country, Sri Lanka produces a huge variety of fruit. There are the usuals – papaya, pineapple, several varieties of mango, passion fruit and over a dozen varieties of bananas. Then there are the unusual – purple-husked mangosteen, rambutan, sapodilla, soursap, guava, beli, varaka – the list goes on.*

Wilpattu National Park

Wilpattu National Park is a complex of lakes called *villus* surrounded by grassy plains and set within scrub jungle. Its biggest draw is the leopard, and the park once enjoyed the best reputation in Sri Lanka for viewing these magnificent big cats. Wilpattu was re-opened in 2003 after a 16-year break, and there are signs that it will be an excellent site for leopard enthusiasts once more. One mammal that is more easily seen at Wilpattu than at any other national park is the Muntjac or Barking Deer. Butterflies recorded here include the Great Eggfly, Great Orange Tip, Glad-eye Bushbrown, Blue Mormon, Common Mormon, Common Rose and Crimson Rose.

RIGHT *Wilpattu is best known for its villus or lakes. The villus have varying degrees of salinity, but most are suitable for drinking by animals. Wilpattu also has riverine forest along the banks of a few streams which run through it. These streams become very important as a source of water for animals during the dry season. The riverine forests also harbour different kinds of birds, butterflies and other fauna, which help to diversify the species found in the park.*

BELOW *Most of the day-time sightings of leopards in national parks are of cubs (up to 18 months old) and sub-adults (18–36 months old). As their mother hunts for them, they lead a relaxed existence. Some cubs become quite tolerant of safari vehicles.*

Butterflies

Sri Lanka is home to 244 species of butterfly. According to Harish Gaonkar, a scientist working at the British Museum of Natural History, 23 of Sri Lanka's butterfly species are only found on the island. He believes another 16 species are confined to the Western Ghats in India and Sri Lanka. Many of these unique species are rare and inhabit the low wetlands.

However, the dry lowlands are also a good habitat for butterflies, especially after the monsoons. A day in one of the sanctuaries, such as those at Annaiwilundawa or Wilpattu, can easily yield around 30 or more species. Even the roadsides are home to good numbers of these gorgeous insects. The tiny Grass Jewel is one of the smallest of Sri Lanka's butterflies, and, as the name suggests, the species is quick to colonize areas where the grass has not been mown. Other small species of butterfly, including the Psyche and Red Pierrot, are also found flitting around the grassy layer. Hiding in sheltered vegetation, even town gardens, is the Common Palmfly. The female of this species can mimic the colouration of two forms of the Plain Tiger, a member of the *Danaidae* family. These butterflies, which are commonly known as Tigers, carry poisons in their body that are absorbed during the larval stage, when the caterpillar feeds on leaves rich in alkaloids. As a result the butterflies are distasteful to birds. Other species, for example the Common Mime and female Danaid Eggfly, take advantage of this quirk of evolution by mimicking these poisonous species.

ABOVE *The Great Eggfly (*Hypolimnas bolina) *is widely distributed up to the mid-hills. It can be seen in good quality forests as well as in urban gardens.*

LEFT *The Tailed Jay (*Graphium agamemnon) *is a very active butterfly, always fluttering rapidly as it sips flowers, or flitting rapidly from one bunch of flowers to another. It seldom stays still as in this picture.*

RIGHT *The Plain Tiger (*Danaus chrysippus*) is one of the commonest butterflies found in home gardens and wayside verges. The tiger larvae accumulate toxic alkaloids which are retained in the body of the adult. Consequently birds avoid eating them.*

BELOW *The Blue Mormon (*Papilio polymnestor*) together with the Common Birdwing (*Troides darsius*) are amongst the two largest butterflies in Sri Lanka. It is widespread, and favours wooded areas.*

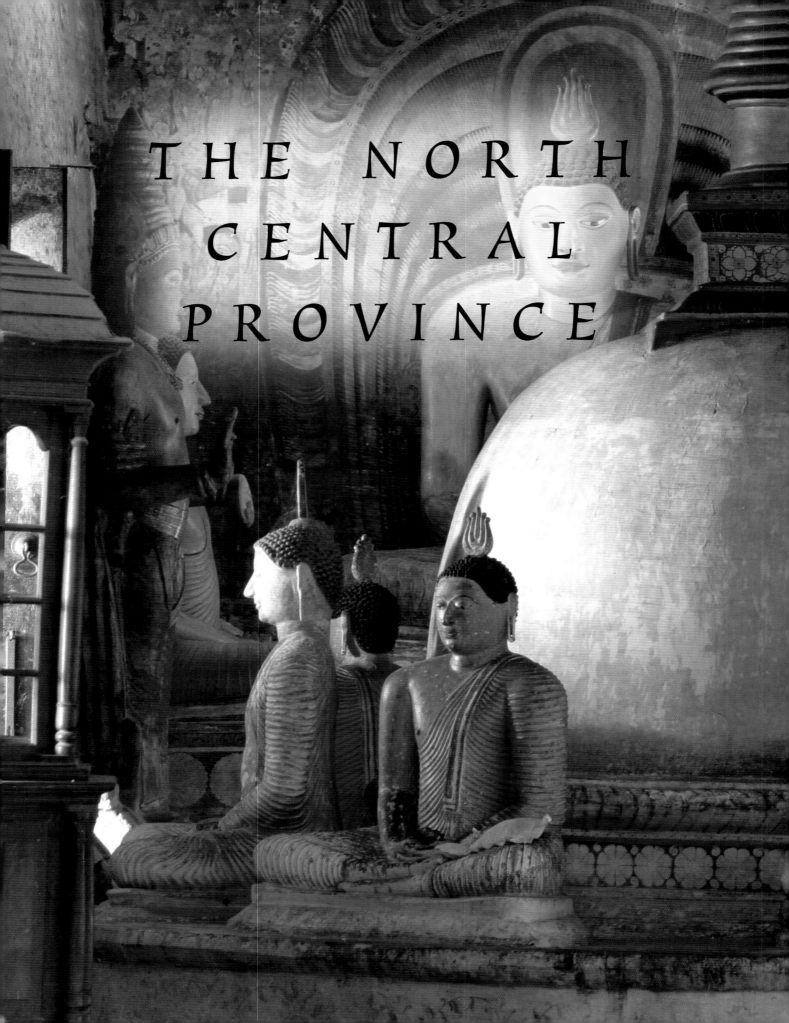

THE NORTH
CENTRAL
PROVINCE

THE NORTH CENTRAL PROVINCE

The North Central Province of Sri Lanka is a treasure trove for cultural buffs and archaeologists. Giant stupas dominate the skylines of ancient cities such as Anuradhapura and Polonnaruwa, and elephants – the giants of the living world – converge in their hundreds for 'the gathering'. The dry, desiccated plains are densely populated, with man-made lakes or tanks, a reminder of a great civilization that had a brilliant grasp of hydraulics.

The magnificent works of the historical engineers and architects have been invaded by the jungle and now provide an excellent refuge for the island's animals. Huge troops of monkeys inhabit the ancient cities, where wildlife and culture have become inseparable.

The Cave Temples of Dambulla

Dambulla leaves a lasting impression on most visitors. This huge geological landmark is formed from two dome-shaped outcrops of rock called inselberge, which rise 160 metres (525 feet) above the surrounding plain. Entering the cool, dimly lit caves, which are hewn into the rock about halfway up the hill, a breathtaking array of murals and Buddhist statues and stonework

PREVIOUS PAGES *Paintings from the 18th and 19th centuries decorate the ceilings of the Maharaja Vihara, the largest of the five caves in the Dambulla Cave Temple Complex. The Maharaja Vihara was founded in the 1st century BC by King Vattagamini Abhaya of the Anuradhapura era. The central sanctuary area has a small stupa surrounded by seated Buddhas.*

BELOW *A decorated verandah with a stupa at one end, borders one of the caves of Dambulla.*

ABOVE *The Maharaja Vihara in Dambulla has been described as one the most dramatic internal spaces in Sri Lankan architecture. One panel of paintings depicts a thousand Buddhas.*

are revealed. Pilgrims clad in white offer flowers and chant prayers, while monks attired in yellow robes go about their serene monastic lives. This heady mix of ancient art and fervent religious activity, combined with the immensely spiritual location, leaves many visitors overwhelmed by the experience.

Although the caves have been in use since prehistoric times, the site's ascendancy as an important monastic centre begins with the story of King Valagambahu, also known as Vattagamini Abhaya. The king took refuge in the caves for 14 years in the 1st century BC during an invasion from India. As he fled the invaders, a Jain priest mocked Valagambahu with the words, 'look, the great black lion is fleeing'. The angered king vowed to destroy the Jain monastery and build a Buddhist monastery in its place once he had driven away the invaders. True to his promise, the victorious Valagambahu constructed a vast Buddhist monastery. Although there is an absence of written records, it is generally believed that the king carved drip ledges and took steps to transform the caves of Dambulla into a beautiful monastery complex in gratitude for his victory over the invaders.

RIGHT *A long decorated verandah runs the length of the five caves currently in use at Dambulla. The caves are in fact separate chambers created by screen walls and partitions.*

Sigiriya – The Rock Palace

Rising 200 metres (650 feet) above the surrounding land, Sigiriya, or Lion Rock, obtains its name from the Sinhala word '*singha giri*'. This giant granite rock is set in an area of stunning natural beauty, surrounded by forest and imbued with an air of mystery. The tragic origins of Sigiriya centre around Prince Kasyappa, the son of King Dhatusena, who reigned AD 459–477. Kasyappa was the king's son by a consort who was not of royal blood. Determined to seize the throne, Kasyappa had his father killed. Mogallana, the Crown Prince and rightful heir to the throne, fled to India in fear of his life. In order to protect himself from attacks from Mogallana, Kasyappa made Sigiriya his capital, building his palace on the summit of the rock.

Kasyappa was an artistic and creative genius who brought his vision of heaven on earth to fruition. Sigiriya has one of the oldest landscaped gardens in the world. The area around the rock was converted into water, boulder and terraced gardens with pools, fountains and terraces. In addition to the beauty of the layout surrounding the rock, the palace itself had a large pool, which is cut from the stone and surrounded by gardens. About halfway up the rock are the famous paintings of the Sigiriya ladies. The urban planning of this city is of considerable interest to archaeologists because of its well-preserved form and excellent design.

BELOW *Sigiriya is one of the most dramatic and important archaeological sites in Asia. A 5th century AD, walled, moated palace complex was centered around this monolith.*

OPPOSITE *Descending from the summit to the Lion Staircase, one faces this dramatic view of the surrounding plains framed by a near vertical rock face. Even today, to build a palace atop Sigiriya would be an extraordinary feat of engineering.*

LEFT *The Boulder Archway of the Boulder Gardens at the base of Sigiriya. The Boulder Gardens depart from the rigid geometry of the Water Gardens and instead take a more organic approach, following the natural topography.*

ABOVE *The paintings of* Apsaras *or celestial maidens on Sigiriya have been the subject of much debate as to whom they actually represented. What survives today are fragments of a once extensive panel of paintings which may have extended 140 m in length.*

RIGHT *The water gardens at Sigiriya are symmetrically planned and feature highly sophisticated hydraulic technologies dating from the early historic period.*

Polonnaruwa, an Ancient Capital

From the 10th century AD, the capital of the island shifted from Anuradhapura to Polonnaruwa. The site was seen by rulers to have more military and strategic advantages than the previous capital. It was better located for meeting a threat from the south, and closer to several important crossings of the Mahaveli River for trading purposes. It was the capital of the island from around AD 993 to 1250.

The Cholas from India, who conquered Anuradhapura in the late 10th century, were the first to make Polonnaruwa the capital of the northern kingdom. After 77 years of Chola rule, a Sinhalese king, Vijayabahu I (1055–1110), seized the north, driving the invaders off the island. Vijayabahu retained Polonnaruwa as his capital. In his 55-year rule he restored irrigation works and was able to bring about a renaissance of Sinhala-Buddhist culture, including the return of Sinhala monks who had fled to Burma.

BELOW *A Buddha sculpture in the Atadage, the first Tooth Relic Shrine built by King Vijayabahu I in the 11th century.*

The greatest king of Polonnaruwa was Parakramabahu I (1153 –1186). During his golden reign the area flourished. Agriculture developed to its highest peak and Sri Lanka became the granary of the east. With this new economic prosperity came several new building projects. The buildings created and constructed during this era were grand and impressive, for example the royal palace, the Lankathilaka image house and the Gal Vihara, with its great sculptures of the Buddha. A great Sri Lankan chronicle called the *Culavamsa*, states that Parakramabahu repaired or built 165 dams, 3,910 canals, 163 major tanks and 2,376 minor tanks. He is most famous for creating the enormous Parakrama Samudra – 'Sea of Parakrama' – a 2,500-hectare (6,200-acre) tank with a capacity of 134 million cubic metres (4,730 cubic feet). He also established a centralized system of administration so that the whole country came under the personal rule of the king.

Nissankamalla, who reigned between 1187–1196, was the last king of Polonnaruwa to rule the whole country. He established king's courts in various districts to settle legal and criminal disputes. He also constructed the beautiful shrines of Vatadage, Hatadage and the Nissankalata Mandapa. The Rankot Stupa is another one of Nissankamalla's achievements.

LEFT *The Lata Mandapaya in the quadrangle of Polonnaruwa was an image house. The elaborate columns are all that remains.*

BELOW *A view of the Lankathilaka, which dates from the 12th century.*

ABOVE *Stone carvings on the columns of the Atadage, a tooth relic shrine.*

LEFT ABOVE *The Thuparama is a vaulted image house in the Quadrangle of Polonnaruwa. It houses a recumbent Buddha.*

LEFT BELOW *The Kiri Vehera built in the 12th century is a heavily plastered brick stupa. It may have been built by Queen Subhadra (Bhaddavati) one of the wives of the great King Parakramabahu.*

OPPOSITE *The Lankathilaka Image House has four false storeys marked on its exterior walls. The Lankathilaka and Kiri Vehera are part of the vast eight hectare Alahana Parivena Monastic Complex.*

LEFT *The stone sculptures of the Buddha at Gal Vihara show a sublimity and finesse which is unrivalled in the world. It is a part of the Northern Monastery or Uttararama founded by the great King Parakramabahu I.*

The Temple Monkeys

Sri Lanka is home to three species of diurnal primates and two nocturnal species. Of the three monkeys active in the daytime, the Hanuman Langur is found mainly in the dry lowlands. It gathers in troops that sometimes number over 50 individuals. At sites within the Cultural Triangle, the area bounded by the ancient capitals of Anuradhapura, Polonnaruwa and Kandy, these temple monkeys have mostly become tolerant of visitors. However, they do not scavenge for food left by visitors, as they are leaf-eaters, as are the aptly named Leaf Monkeys. However, the Toque Monkeys do scavenge and can become quite aggressive. These Polonnaruwa primates are the subject of one of the longest running field-studies in the world, which has run for over 35 years.

The Purple-faced Leaf Monkey provides a good example of how the different climatic zones on the island have created the type of variation one would normally expect to see in a continental landmass. Four sub-species of the Leaf Monkey are unique to Sri Lanka, despite the island's tiny size. The species living at higher altitudes has a distinctive shaggy coat and is named the Bear Monkey. The Bear Monkeys are usually very shy animals, scampering away at the slightest signs of a human. However, at the Hakgala Botanical Gardens, they are used to people.

BELOW *Hanuman Langurs* (Presbytis entellus) *are leaf-eating monkeys, that live in societies dominated by an alpha male.*

RIGHT *Toque Macaque (*Macaca sinica*) numbers have grown at an astonishing rate in the archaeological reserve of Polonnaruwa. These monkeys have been subject to a continuous scientific study over three decades.*

BELOW *The endemic Purple-faced Leaf Monkey (*Presbytis senex*) has four races, all of which are shy. Polonnaruwa is a good place to see the Northern sub-species which has become somewhat used to human proximity.*

Wasgomuwa National Park

Wasgomuwa National Park is to the south of Polonnaruwa and to the north of the Knuckles Range and the Matale foothills. This wonderful habitat consists of thick forest that hugs the River Mahaveli and dry monsoon forest in the low foothills.

Birds that can be spotted here include the Ceylon Junglefowl, Ceylon Grey Hornbill, Brown-capped Babbler, Blue-faced Malkoha, Lesser Adjutant, Grey-headed Fish-Eagle and Brown Fish Owl. Mammals found in the park include the Elephant, Leopard, Sloth Bear, Golden Jackal, Spotted Deer, Sambar, Mongoose, Civet, Slender Loris and Hanuman Langur.

Wasgomuwa National Park is not as visited as the more popular parks such as Wilpattu, Yala, Bundala and Uda Walawe. Those in search of a more tranquil wilderness experience may prefer it for this reason. However with access to the park being improved from Polonnaruwa, it is likely that the park which is good for elephants will gain popularity. The elephants in the park are also 'wilder'. They are more prone to charge vehicles and generally express their displeasure towards humans. This wariness is probably a result of conflict with farmers when they wander outside the park. Increasingly, electric fences are being used to confine the movement of elephants.

BELOW The Grey-headed Fish-eagle (Ichthyophaga ichthyaetus) is a nationally endangered bird. It is found in small numbers in the tanks or ancient man-made lakes in the dry lowlands.

Wasgomuwa National Park may have one of the highest densities of the Sloth Bear (Melursus ursinus) in Sri Lanka. But as it is a nocturnal animal, visitors are more likely to see tracks and signs of it than have a visual encounter.

Wasgomuwa National Park on the north central plains is overshadowed by the northern periphery of the Knuckles massif. The Park is home to significant numbers of elephants.

Minneriya National Park and 'The Gathering'

Sri Lankan wildlife defies conventional wisdom. Small islands are not supposed to have large animals. But someone forgot to tell this to the planet's largest terrestrial mammal – the elephant. Not only is the species still found in reasonable numbers in Sri Lanka, the largest concentration of Asian Elephants, a seasonal gathering, takes place on the island.

Every year, 'the gathering' takes place in Minneriya National Park in the north central

province of Sri Lanka. As the dry season fastens its grip on the arid lowlands, leaves wither and fall in the dry deciduous forests and waterholes evaporate into cakes of cracked and parched mud, the elephants must move on in search of food and water. Sometimes numbering over 300 individuals, the elephants converge at the receding shores of Minneriya Tank. It is an awe-inspiring site. Nowhere else in the world will one find such a high concentration of wild Asian Elephants packed into just a few square kilometres.

LEFT ABOVE *Minneriya is a wonderful place to observe young elephants interacting with each other.*

LEFT BELOW *A typical herd of elephants numbering between 40 and 80 individuals which coalesce into larger herds, exceeding 100 individuals during the peak of the gathering. At its peak, over 300 elephants can be within a kilometre of each other.*

RIGHT *An elephant's trunk is an amazing tool. It's an extra limb for picking things up, a weapon for use in combat and comes in handy as a portable shower head and hose.*

BELOW *During the gathering, the herds inevitably go to the water to drink and to bathe, in the evening. The staff of the Department of Wildlife Conservation ensure that safari jeeps maintain an adequate distance to avoid disturbing the elephants who are going to the water.*

Anuradhapura, an Ancient Capital

ABOVE *A little girl unwraps the petals of a Lotus flower to be offered at temple.*

BELOW *The sacred Bo Tree at Anuradhapura is the oldest historically documented tree in the world.*

The scale and size of Anuradhapura was comparable to a modern city. To truly appreciate its dimensions only an aerial view really does it justice. Over the last two decades, this ancient city has been subject to a major conservation project and some key monuments have been restored. The restoration has been undertaken with the aim of leaving intact many of the trees that have grown around the ruins. This does mean that some of the grandeur of the site is lost, as there is no open, sweeping view of the immense city. But it is the right decision, as the trees and plants of the scrub jungle lend much-needed shade in the burning heat and provide the site with the charm and mystique of a legendary 'lost city'.

Anuradhapura is considered the most extensive and important of the ancient cities in the north-central region. It served as a capital city of this area for over 1,000 years, and was the residence of many ancient kings from 377 BC. Pandukabhaya, who reigned from 377–307 BC, first made Anuradhapura the capital, naming it after the constellation Anuradha. During the later reign of Devanampiyatissa (250–210 BC) Buddhism was introduced to Sri Lanka and the city rose to greatness, becoming a centre for Buddhist devotion. The great Sinhalese kings Dutugemunu (161–137 BC), Vasabha (AD 121–171) and Mahasena (AD 274–301) all reigned from Anuradhapura.

The kings of Anuradhapura engaged in impressive irrigation projects, building tanks – 'wewas' – and canals to provide water for rice cultivation. The tanks are impressive feats of engineering, particularly given that they were built between about AD 60–300.

The Giant Stupas of Anuradhapura

Just as Egypt is associated with its pyramids, Sri Lanka is perhaps best associated with its distinctive stupas. Nowhere are these more conspicuous or of such staggering proportions than at Anuradhapura. The stupas of Jetavana, Abayagiri and Ruwanveliseya soar upward, creating a unique skyline. This impressive sight is best viewed from across an ancient *wewa*, such as Baswakkulama, one of the many giant reservoirs built by the ancient kings to irrigate these dry plains. To the west of Anuradhapura lies Mihintale, where Buddhism was first introduced to the island. This is one of the most important monastery complexes in the country and is set amidst a small range of hills.

Built in one of six shapes, for example bell-shaped or bubble-shaped, these huge structures are excellent examples of Buddhist architecture and demonstrate the high standard of building techniques employed during this period. The base of the 4th-century Jetavana stupa has a diameter of 112 metres (367 feet) and it is almost 122 metres (400 feet) high. It is the largest stupa in the world.

RIGHT ABOVE *The Ruvanweliseya or the Great Stupa stands 91 metres (300 feet) tall and is the smallest of the three largest ancient brick structures.*

RIGHT BELOW *The oldest of the stupas in Anuradhapura is the Thuparama. The collarbone of the Buddha is believed to be enshrined here.*

THE
CENTRAL
HILLS

THE CENTRAL HILLS

S ri Lanka's second most important city, Kandy, is found in the central hills of the island. The last of the historical kingdoms to fall to colonial invaders, it has remained a bastion of religion and culture. Scattered in and around Kandy are religious complexes that are widely admired for their medieval architecture.

The central hills also mark an important transition from the humid lowlands to the highlands. This region is rich in wildlife, although many of the original forests have been lost to cultivation.

Kandy

Situated 500 metres (1,640 feet) above sea level, Kandy is Sri Lanka's second largest city, but it is quite different from Colombo due to its position in the hills and cooler climate. At the heart of the city, Kandy lake provides a tranquil setting, with houses built on the slopes of the hills

PREVIOUS PAGES *A view of the Octagonal Room of the Temple of the Tooth Relic from the Natha Devale complex.*

BELOW *The pink facade of a mosque down one of Kandy's streets. Like with any city centre, parking has become a huge problem and the visitor should take to the streets on foot or on a trishaw (tuk tuk).*

ABOVE *Two Buddhist monks walk past a cluster of signs advertising the services of lawyers, down D. S. Senanayake Veediya.*

and looking down onto the water. Kandy is a pleasant place for walking, whether in the town itself, in the surrounding hills or in the Peradeniya Botanical Gardens. The city is a major tourist centre and is home to the famous Temple of the Tooth Relic.

Kandy also plays host to the spectacular *Esala Perahera* festival, which is held for ten days at the end of July and beginning of August. It is a colourful celebration and world-famous event, including a wonderful procession of magnificently dressed elephants and dancers among many other delights. The highlight is when the Tooth Relic of the Buddha is borne through the streets of Kandy on the back of an ornately decorated tusker, which is guided by officials of the temple.

The Peradeniya Botanical Gardens are extensive and boast many indigenous and rare plants. 'Peradeniya has almost everything from Kipling's "Palm" to "Pine" thanks to the climate', states Roland Raven-Hart in his book *Ceylon: History in Stone* (1964). The gardens have an excellent collection of orchids and a famous avenue of royal palms. The herb garden contains various herbs used in local medicine, for, as Robert Knox, a 17th-century Englishman who was held prisoner by the Kandyan kings for 19 years, remarked, 'the woods are their apothecaries shops'.

LEFT Ulpenge *or the Queen's Bathing Pavilion. The British added another storey and filled in the stone bathing pond to make a library.*

Temple of the Tooth Relic

The Sacred Tooth Relic, which is housed in Kandy's Temple of the Tooth Relic, is a Buddhist object of veneration and the most important religious relic in Sri Lanka. The site is also one of the most sacred places for Buddhists from all over the world.

From ancient times, Sri Lankan kings kept the Sacred Tooth Relic in their kingdoms as a symbol of power. It is recorded that the Tooth Relic was first brought to the island by Prince Dhantha and Princess Hemamali, during the reign of Kirti Sri Meghavanna (AD 301–328). It is a traditional belief that whoever takes possession of the Tooth Relic has the power to rule the people of the island.

King Vimala Dharma Suriya I constructed the original temple in the 16th century, when the relic first came to Kandy. Several decades later, the building was renovated by King Narendra Singha, and it is this building that stands today. Additions were made to its design by various kings. The moat, gateway, drawbridge and octagonal room were added by Sri Vikrama Rajasingha and the inner shrine was built by Kirti Sri Rajasingha. The temple is heavily ornamented, with carvings on the stone doorways, painted timber ceilings and timber doorways richly inlaid with metal and ivory carvings.

The temple is at the focus of the annual *Esala Perahera*, one of the grandest cultural pageants in the world.

OPPOSITE ABOVE *The moat at the entrance to the Dalada Maligawa or Temple of the Tooth Relic.*

OPPOSITE BELOW *A mahout guides his elephant past the Temple of the Tooth Relic complex. The Octagon Room or Pattirippuwa was built by the last king of Kandy, Sri Vikrama Rajasingha. It now holds a valuable collection of Ola leaf manuscripts.*

RIGHT ABOVE *A vaulted passage leads to the inner courtyard of the Temple of the Tooth Relic.*

RIGHT BELOW *Devotees make offerings on the ground floor or climb up one floor of the inner sanctum.*

RIGHT *A view of the interior of the 'Image House' or Budhu Ge of the Natha Devale complex, which is opposite the Temple of the Tooth Relic.*

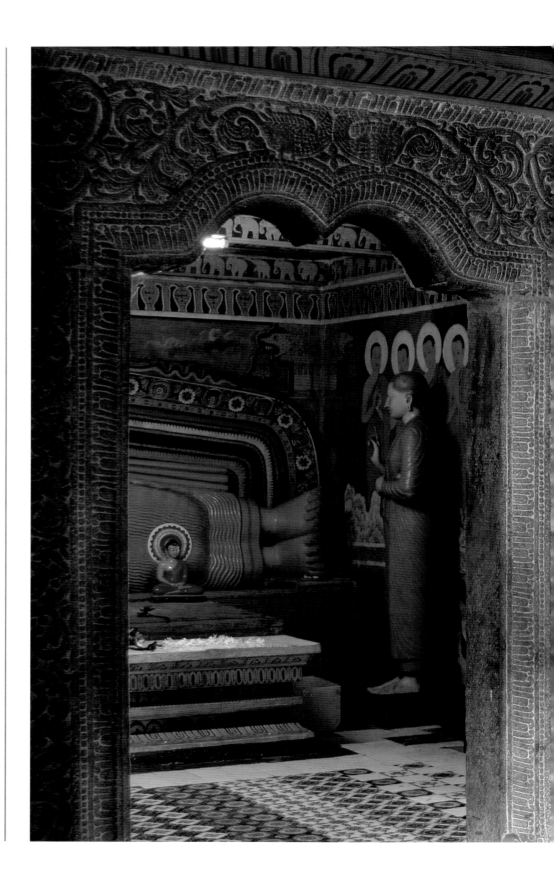

Temples to the West of Kandy

This temple circuit covers some of the most famous and well-known ancient temples in the area around Kandy. They are close enough to the city to be visited on an excursion lasting just a few hours.

Gadaladeniya Vihara

BELOW The Gadaladeniya, stone-built image house is one of the most important buildings of the 14th century. It is South Indian in style.

The site at Gadaladeniya is distinctive, consisting of a central stupa, with smaller stupas sited at its cardinal points. Kandyan-style steep, sloping roofs cover the structures, supported by thick white columns. Carvings of elephants adorn the otherwise plain walls. At each of the cardinal

points the small shrine rooms contain seated Buddhas and many ancient murals in a state of decay. The main temple clearly shows an Indian influence. Although a Buddhist temple, it was constructed in the style of a Hindu temple by the Dravidian architect Ganeswaracharya, who was employed in 1344 by King Buvanekabahu IV (1341–1351). It is built entirely of stone, including the *sikhara*, or upper floor, which is in the shape of a *dagaba*.

LEFT ABOVE *Colourful prayer flags hung on a sacred Bo Tree (Ficus religiosa) at Gadaladeniya.*

LEFT BELOW *It is considered an honour for a family to have a son being schooled as a monk. Some enter training at a very young age. The other members of the family visit them regularly and follow their progress.*

Lankathilake Vihara

About 4 kilometres (2 miles) from Gadaladeniya is the Lankathilaka *vihara*. The temple is entered though a *vahalkada* or gateway, a wooden, roofed structure supported by stone columns. The stepped design of the tiled roof is immediately striking. Tusked elephants are sculpted into recesses of the walls of the temple.

At the back of the temple, entry to the image house, a shrine that contains images for Buddhist worship, is through a huge *makara thorana* (arch of dragons) flanked by lions. Stepping through the wooden doorway, a 750-year-old Buddha becomes visible, seated under another colourful *makara thorana*. On either side of the seated Buddha there are two standing Buddhas. Murals cover the walls and the roof is embroidered with flower motifs.

The temple was constructed in 1344, on an exposed area of natural rock. It was built by Senadhilankara, the Chief Minister of King Buvanekabahu IV (1341–57). The architect, Sthaptharaya, was from southern India, but the Sinhalese style was adopted for the building. The building originally had four floors, only two of which survive and only the ground floor is in use. The tiled roof that covers these two levels was added in the 19th century. There are six *devalas* (Hindu shrines) around the inner Buddhist temple. A unique feature of the temple is that all the deities are represented with their wives or consorts.

There are six devalas (shrines) around the temple. One of them is dedicated to Saman, a pre-Buddhist divinity, who is believed to reside on Adam's Peak. Both Buddhists and Hindus worship at the Devalas, to deities who are attributed with different powers.

ABOVE *There is a long association between elephants and religious and cultural pageants in Sri Lanka. A relief of elephants decorates the ground floor of the Lankathilaka Temple.*

LEFT *The Lankthilaka Temple is architecturally unique in Sri Lanka. It is close enough to Kandy to warrant an excursion from Kandy or a detour if travelling from Colombo. A visit to Lankathilake can easily be combined with visits to Gadaladeniya and Embkke.*

Embekke Devale

About 4 kilometres (2 miles) from Lankathilaka is Embekke Devale. The temple is entered through a covered porch that is supported by carved wooden pillars. It is believed to have been constructed in the 14th or 15th centuries, and formed the audience halls of the Gampola kings. It was later converted into a temple dedicated to the Sinhalese war god, Kartikeya. The *dig ge* (drumming hall) is a wooden, roofed structure that is supported by numerous intricately carved wooden columns.

The former audience hall has seven pairs of pillars on both sides. About two-thirds of the way up each pillar, or *gammalu*, is a square carving of four faces. The carved pillars reveal a variety of designs, including figures of dancers, birds, animals and soldiers. The pillar capitals are carved lotus flowers. All the carvings are still in very good condition and have been reproduced extensively.

The main shrine is at the far end of the audience hall. It has a sequinned tapestry depicting Kataragama, or Skanda, the Hindu god of war. This *devala* was built by King Vikramabahu III (1357–1374) one of the Gampola kings.

RIGHT ABOVE A wooden carving depicts a traditional form of sport: wrestling.

BELOW Embekke Devale has some of the finest examples of medieval Kandyan wood carving. It was built in the 14th century and is dedicated to the god Skanda.

THE
HIGHLANDS

THE HIGHLANDS

A distinctive feature of Sri Lanka's topography is the 'stepped structure' – the golden fringe of sandy beaches continues inland for some distance and then rises abruptly to form the central hills, which rise to elevations of between 500 metres (1,640 feet) and 1,800 metres (5,900 feet). These hills take another step up to form the highlands, which are rugged and very uneven in profile. The conquest of the highlands is a relatively new phenomenon and it was not until the 19th century that much of the area was colonized. Although scattered settlements existed, it was the British who pushed their way into the highland interior, building roads and railroads. This colonization was not done in the spirit of exploration, but for money.

The British saw the forest-clad peaks and thought they could make mountains of money by opening the area up to plant coffee. When the coffee crops were wiped out by blight, the colonists switched to tea. Tea is what travellers are most likely to see as the mountain roads wend their way through one hairpin bend after another. The crop remains an important source of hard currency for the country, and much of the economy of the highland areas is driven by it. The highlands are also an important source of vegetables and cut flowers, many of which can only be grown successfully at these high altitudes.

PREVIOUS PAGES *Morning mist lifting off the mountains, on the way up to Hortons Plains National Park. During certain times of the year, the plains are shrouded in mist and drizzle.*

BELOW *The 80-metre (262-foot) high St Clairs Falls is on the Hatton to Nuwara Eliya Road. The 'stepped structure' of Sri Lanka's topography has resulted in a large number of waterfalls in the highlands.*

Nuwara Eliya

Nuwara Eliya meaning 'City of Light' was developed by the British and was intended to resemble home, as is evident in the architecture of the houses, the park layouts, the trout streams and the golf course. Many British planters lived on tea estates around the city, inhabiting traditional English country houses with fireplaces and large, well-maintained gardens. Driving past the houses built in Georgian or Queen Anne style, one is frequently reminded of the town's colonial past, hence the name 'Little England'.

Nuwara Eliya is 80 kilometres (50 miles) from Kandy, but much higher at 1,890 metres (6,200 feet) above sea level. Due to the mountain location, it is cooler, particularly in January and February, when temperatures can fall to freezing.

Nuwara Eliya is a popular hill resort and provides a pleasant base to explore a number of Sri Lanka's higher-altitude wildlife sites. There are some attractive walks to be had in the town's parks, including Victoria Park, which is centrally located. Hakgala Botanical Gardens, which are about 9 kilometres (5 miles) away on the road to Welimada, are worth a visit; although they are small, they very pleasant and famous for their beautiful roses. Nuwara Eliya's 18-hole St Andrew's golf course is said to be one of the finest in Asia. The Hill Club is an interesting dining experience, as one needs to be 'properly' dressed to be served in style by waiters wearing smart white uniforms. Another site well worth visiting is Horton Plains National Park

ABOVE *A statue at the Sitha Temple near Hakgala. The temple celebrates the story of Hanuman the Monkey God who rescued Sitha, the wife of Rama.*

RIGHT *Some of the finest tea estates in Sri Lanka are around Nuwara Eliya. Tamil women pick by hand the fresh shoots.*

BELOW *Tea remains very important to Sri Lanka's economy, and sights such as this are common in the highland area.*

Horton Plains National Park

Sri Lanka's second- and third-highest peaks, Thotupola Kanda (2,357 metres/7,733 feet) and Kirigalpotta (2,389 metres/7,838 feet), are situated in Horton Plains National Park. Three important rivers, the Mahaveli, Kelani and Walawe, originate in this region. The highlights for walkers are the World's End and Baker's waterfalls.

Endemic birds found in the park include the Ceylon Whistling Thrush, Ceylon White-eye, Ceylon Wood Pigeon and Dusky-blue Flycatcher. The trees are dominated by Keena, *Syzgium rotundifolium*, *Syzgium sclerophyllum* and species from the *Lauracea* family. Giant ferns are also a conspicuous feature. Numbers of Sambar, the island's largest deer, have soared in the last decade, resulting in a corresponding increase of their main predator, the leopard.

BELOW *At 2,243 metres (7,359 feet), Adam's Peak is Sri Lanka's fifth highest peak. The abode of the divine deity Saman, surpasses all other peaks in importance with a long history of religious significance. The peak is sacred to Buddhists, Muslims and Christians.*

THE
SOUTH

THE SOUTH

It's a common misconception that southern Sri Lanka is a culturally bankrupt relation of the past glories of the ancient capitals of the north central plains or the more recent achievements of the Kandyan highlands. But in fact, the southern kingdom of Ruhuna had its own king under a feudal system that lasted many centuries. When the great King Vijayabahu recaptured Polonnaruwa from the Chola invaders, he began his conquest by taking Ruhuna. With its Dutch Fort, Galle is an important cultural site and has lately become a fashionable residence for expatriate investors.

The south has some of the best of the national parks and wildlife sanctuaries. Kalametiya Sanctuary, Bundala and Ruhuna National Parks are all pivotal for the conservation of tens of thousands of wintering birds. The lakes in the dry south teem with ducks and the little brown shorebirds that have a compelling fascination for birdwatchers.

Galle

Situated 118 kilometres (73 miles) from Colombo, Galle, on the south coast, is a town steeped in history. Its natural harbour has served as an important port from historical times to the present day. The Victorian historian Sir Emerson Tennant claimed that Galle was the ancient biblical city of Tarshish. The city is said to have done trade with King Solomon, who supposedly obtained gems, spices and peacocks from the Persians and Egyptians who traded here. Ibn Battuta, the great Moroccan traveller, is also on the guest roll of famous visitors to the port, having visited the island in 1344. In 1505 a Portuguese

fleet led by Lorenzo de Almeida, which was heading for the Maldives, drifted in to Galle accidentally. It is said that on hearing a cock crowing (*galo* is the Portuguese for cockrel) they gave the town its name. Another explanation for the port's name is that it came from the Sinhala word for a rock – *gala* – plenty of which are found in the harbour area.

The Dutch Fort

The old Dutch Fort, which surrounds the older part of the town, sits on a promontory three sides of which face out to sea. The ramparts of the fort are over 2.5 kilometres (1 mile) long and provide a pleasant and interesting route for a walk.

The Dutch Fort's origins lie in an earlier fortification that was built by the Portuguese. When they arrived in Galle, it was already a thriving port and it was not until 1587 that the Portuguese were able to control the town. Unfortunately for the Portuguese, the Dutch overthrew them to take control in 1640. The Dutch had a major impact on Galle and their stamp still remains. Houses with wide doorways and gabled windows were built in the Dutch style, and brick-lined sewers were constructed, which were flushed out twice a day by the rising and falling of the tide.

The present government offices were once the Dutch 'factory' and the original hospital building still stands on Hospital Street. Cinnamon was stored for shipment under an archway that features a Dutch coat of arms and is inscribed with the date 1687. The Dutch-built fort was handed over to the British in 1796. The vast fort remains an important monument to the Dutch colonial era. It is a UNESCO World Heritage site, one of the first to be declared on the basis of it being a living cultural monument.

ABOVE *A detail of a stained glass window from the Dutch Reform Church in the Galle Fort.*

RIGHT *The Dutch Reform Church (Groote Kerk) in Galle was completed around 1755, on the site of an earlier Portuguese capuchin convent.*

The Rainforests of Galle

Galle can be seen as the gateway to rainforest tourism in Sri Lanka because it has been served three trump cards. The Kanneliya-Nakiyadeniya-Dediyagala rainforest complex, known simply as Kanneliya, is one of the largest remaining wet lowland rainforests in Sri Lanka. It is about an hour and fifteen minutes from Galle. Although it was heavily logged in the 1970s, it still remains rich in flora and fauna. The Kottawa Rainforest and Arboretum is no more than half an hour's drive from Galle. It is a part of the Kottawa Kombala Conservation Forest, which covers some 1,800 hectares (4,447 acres). It has a wide track that runs for a kilometre or less through the gloom of the rainforest.

Also about half an hour away is the Hiyare Biodiversity Park, which is administered by the Galle Municipal Council and is set around the forest fringing the Hiyare Reservoir. It adjoins the relatively small Kottawa Kombala rainforest, which is under the jurisdiction of the Forest Department. Hiyare's reservoir is bordered by 240 hectares (600 acres) of secondary lowland rainforest.

The southern race of the endemic Purple-faced Leaf Monkey and Grizzled Indian Squirrel are the mammals visitors are most likely to see in Galle's rainforests. Other mammals such the Mouse-deer, and the endemic and nocturnal Red Loris, are present but hard to see. Endemic reptiles found here include the Earless Lizard, which is relatively easy to spot. Kottawa is also a good place for the spectacular Hump-nosed Lizard. A displaying male is a dramatic sight, with his extended gular sac. Much harder to pick out in the leaf litter, is the Rough-nosed Horned Lizard.

PAGES 118–119 *The stilt fishermen of the south are a famous sight. They perch on poles embedded in the seabed and use a rod and line.*

Yala (Ruhuna) National Park

Yala is undoubtedly Sri Lanka's most visited national park and it is the best in Sri Lanka for viewing a wide diversity of animals. It is a wonderful place, with a spectrum of habitats from scrub jungle to lakes and brackish lagoons to river habitats. Ruhuna National Park is divided into five blocks of which, Block 1, Yala West, is open to the public for most of the year.

The flora is typical of the dry monsoon forest in the southern belt. Plains are interspersed with pockets of forest containing many species of trees, including Palu, Satin, Weera, Maila, Maliththan, Kohomba and Divul. The park is also good for spotting dry zone birds, such as the Indian and Great Thick-knees, Sirkeer and Blue-faced Malkohas and Malabar Pied Hornbill. A day's birding in the park during the winter can yield an impressive count of around 100 species.

The biggest draws in Yala are elephants, leopards and Sloth Bears. A recent study has shown that Yala has one the highest densities of leopards in the world. A game-spotting drive could yield an incredible species count, including the Black-naped Hare, Spotted Deer, Sambar, Hanuman Langur, Toque Monkey, Stripe-necked and Ruddy Mongooses, wild pig, Golden Jackal, Land and Water Monitors and Marsh Crocodile. At the end of the north-east monsoon in February, the park is also very good for spotting butterflies.

ABOVE *The Golden Jackal (*Canis aureus*) is one of the small carnivores found in Yala. The Sri Lankan 'Black-backed' race is distinct from its Indian mainland counterparts.*

LEFT *Large numbers of Spotted Deer (*Axis axis*) provide the prey base to support one of the highest densities of leopards in the world at Yala.*

OPPOSITE *The Hump-nosed Lizard (*Lyriocephalus scutatus*) is a very special lizard, being the only member of its genus. It is found only in Sri Lanka, mainly in the lowland rainforests, and to a lesser extent in the mid-hills. Rainforests, a mere half an hour's drive from Galle allow visitors to find it.*

LEFT *The Ranawara (*Cassia auriculata) *is a common medicinal plant in Yala which holds flowers throughout the year.*

BELOW (TOP) *Lesser Adjutant (*Leptoptilos javanicus)*, an endangered bird is found in small numbers in the dry zone national parks.*

BELOW (BOTTOM) *Heen Caramba (*Carissa spinarum) *with its bunches of white flowers is one of the more common flowering plants in the dry zone.*

Leopards

The leopard is one of the most beautiful and enigmatic mammals in the world. It is the most widespread of the big cat family, found from eastern Asia to sub-Saharan Africa. Of all the big cats, it is the most adaptable, found in a diversity of habitats from very arid areas, such as deserts, to the heights of Africa's Mount Kilimanjaro.

The leopard found in Sri Lanka is an endemic sub-species and it is largely confined to the national parks and reserves. The national parks of Yala and Wilpattu in the dry lowlands are the best places to see these cats, although they sometimes ascend up to the highlands and can be seen in Horton Plains National Park.

Because of their adaptability, stealth and cunning, they are found in habitats where even some of the smaller wild cats are not present. They demonstrate a remarkable resilience and continue to occupy forested habitats very close to a human populace. As recently as 2004, reports were received of leopards coming down to Kandy Lake, in the heart of the town, to drink water. Leopards have also been seen within a few hundred metres of the town centre of Nuwara Eliya, a settlement positioned within an area of high biodiversity.

In Yala National Park, in the last few years a cub, or possibly a pair of cubs, has proved tolerant of vehicles, giving photographers some remarkable opportunities to photograph this elusive species. Until recently, it was not realized that many of the daytime sightings of leopards in national parks such as Yala and Wilpattu were actually sub-adults rather than fully grown specimens. The confusion arose because a male cub aged 18 months is as big as its mother.

ABOVE *Every year in Yala one or more leopard sub-adults perform for the cameras. After about 18 months of age, they become secretive and nocturnal like the adults.*

121

Bundala National Park

Bundala National Park is a mix of scrub jungle and sand dunes that borders the sea. Its beaches are an important nesting site for turtles, and its lagoons contain good numbers of birds and crocodiles.

During the northern winter, large numbers of migrant birds arrive at Bundala. The flora consists of dry acacia scrub, comprising Andara, Kukurumana, Eraminiya and Karamba. The scrub forest trees include Maila, Maliththan, Weera, Palu and Kohomba. Mammals likely to be seen include the elephant, Spotted Deer, Hanuman Langur, Golden Jackal, Black-naped Hare and wild pig. Olive Ridley and Leatherback Turtles, and more rarely Hawksbill and Green Turtles, visit the beaches to lay eggs.

BELOW *Stands of Thakkada (Scaevola sericea) serve to stabilize the ever shifting sand dunes. The sand dunes are a habitat for specialised animals such as the Sand Lizard (Sitana ponticeriana).*

RIGHT ABOVE *Sanderling* (Calidris alba) *are diminutive migrant waders. They have a habit of running to and from with the waves breaking on the shore line.*

RIGHT BELOW *Wara* (Calotropis gigantea) *is a common plant on the coasts and where the soils are poor in nutrients.*

INDEX

ACKNOWLEDGEMENTS

Many people have assisted me over the years in my quest to discover my homeland, Sri Lanka. My friends and especially my wife Nirma and two daughters Maya and Amali have been patient with my innumerable forays into the field. My Aunt Vijita, sister Manori and Uncle Dodwell got me started off in photography. Many friends, naturalists, guides, trackers and safari jeep drivers have assisted my photography in the field.

This book would not have been possible without the support of all of my colleagues at Jetwing. Hiran Cooray my friend, mentor and colleague deserves special mention. He has been supportive of my unconventional multi-tasking techniques, which involves skilful evasion of meetings. I also owe a big thanks to Chandrika Maelge, Ajanthan Shanthiratnam, Ayanthi Samarajewa, Renuka Batagoda, Aruni Hewage, Shehani Seneviratne and L.S. De Silva Gunasekera, the Eco Holidays team. Their efficiency creates space for me to write about and photograph the beauty of Sri Lanka.

I have borrowed sections of manuscript used earlier in *The Magic of Sri Lanka* (New Holland) and also extracts from a book under preparation on the wildlife of Sri Lanka for Bradt Publications. I also thank Vijita de Silva, Tara Wikramanayake and Roland Silva for proofing and comments on the text.

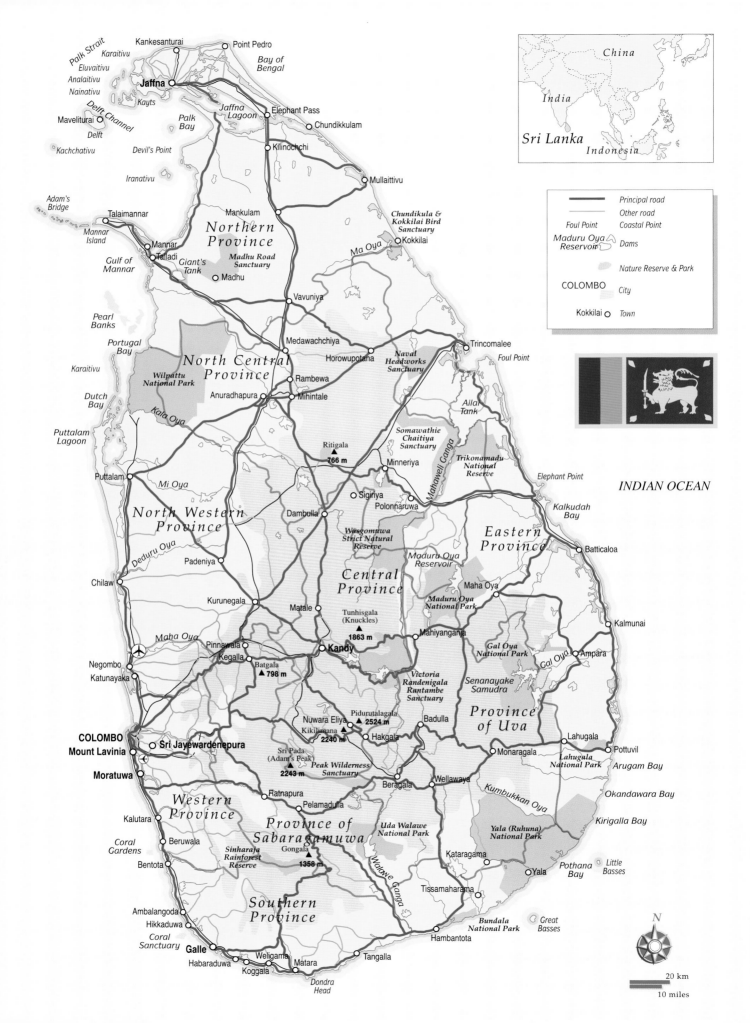